Davett

STRIKE AT THE HEART

STRIKE AT THE HEART

BY
EMMA DARCY

MILLS & BOON LIMITED
Eton House, 18-24 Paradise Road
Richmond, Surrey TW9 1SR

For Taurus with Leo rising—
who inspired this book and has struck
at the heart of all we have written—
a small token of our admiration and gratitude

CHAPTER ONE

NOISE pollution! That's what it was. A crude, barbaric crime against the peace and quiet of the countryside. But of course Sunny King knew there was no police station within easy reach. He knew it was perfectly safe for him to carry on any sort of depraved orgy for as long as he liked, without any consideration to bird or beast or person unfortunate enough to be his neighbour. That was undoubtedly why he had come to St Alban's, surrounding himself with enough property to ensure privacy. It was a malicious trick of fate that he had chosen to buy the property next to hers.

If only it wasn't so damned hot! On a cooler night she could have shut the doors and windows, blocking out the nerve-jangling volume of sound. But no! He had to pick the hottest night of the year to have his rotten house-warming party. It probably suited him. All his fancy guests were undoubtedly prancing naked to the primitive beat of that rock band. They would have to be drunk or drugged to stand the noise. Every amplifier the band had was turned up to maximum output. Jackie wondered how one went about acquiring a plastic bomb.

Her house was like a baker's oven: airless, stifling, oppressive. She could feel perspiration trickling down her back; the light cotton nightie was sticking to her in places. How the boys had been able to sleep in this heat, with that racket going on, was almost incredible, but there'd been no sound from them since she'd ordered them to bed.

Here she was, virtually stewing in her own juices, no closer to sleep than she had been two hours ago. And it was now past one in the morning. For how much longer was that heavy rock music going to blare? Probably until dawn, she decided, kicking irritably at the hot sheets.

In a burst of frustration Jackie rolled off the bed, stomped out to the veranda and glared across at Sunny King's property. Sunny King! What a ridiculous name for a man! Yet it suited the egocentric, show-off type of person he was. And what else could be expected of the latest shining star in the movie world?

The most successful producer/director of films in Australia, the local newspaper had proclaimed when he had favoured St Alban's by choosing to live in the area. The article had been most effusive about his marvellous career, but in actual fact he had only hit the big-time with his last two movies. Apparently blood-curdling violence was big box office, and Sunny King had capitalised on it by creating a cult-figure hero who went about slaughtering enemies like a killing machine.

It disgusted Jackie that such a hero could have so much popular appeal. Even her own sons thought the one-eyed avenger, Dirk Vescum, was terrific. It disgusted her even further that Sunny King had got rich by tapping the baser instincts in people. And right now she felt a monumental disgust that she had to put up with his living next door to her.

He was supposed to have come here because the relative isolation of the countryside would give him the peace and quiet necessary to work on ideas for his movies. Peace and quiet! She wished she could give him peace and quiet all right. In a padded cell!

Only a madman could have built such a monstrosity of a house. He even had the arrogance to call it King's Folly. With all its stupid turrets it was more like Court Jester's Folly. The man had no sensitivity towards the environment, no sensitivity at all.

Jackie's mouth curled in disdain at Sunny King and all he stood for. These newly rich people despoiled everything they touched. They had no manners, no civility, no sophistication. He had not even had the courtesy to return her neighbourly call. Admittedly only his secretary, Trevor Haines, had been in residence at the time, but he had said he would pass on her greetings.

But the great Sunny King hadn't bothered to introduce himself to his next-door neighbour. Nor invite her and the children to his house-warming party. Not that she would have gone, but he could have given her the pleasure of refusing his invitation. The man was crass!

It was a terrible shame to see the way the whole district was losing its identity. The old families were dying off or selling out, and the newcomers had no real respect for the land and its traditions. All they wanted was the luxury of hectares of land around their ostentatious homes. The history of the settlement of the Macdonald's River and the village of St Alban's meant little or nothing to them. They had swooped in because of the far more attractive asset of being within easy commuting distance to Sydney.

Jackie heaved a resentful sigh and turned her back on the offensive sight and sound of Sunny King's party. She wandered restlessly along the veranda which ran around three sides of her small weatherboard house. There was a waft of breeze coming from the south. If she dragged the spare mattress out on to the veranda, she might get some sleep.

Ten minutes later she had managed to pull the bedding through the front doorway and was comfortably settled on it. Even her pillow felt cooler. There was definitely a light breeze coming over the front steps. She stuffed wadded cotton-wool into her ears, which diminished the noise considerably, and it wasn't long before she drifted off to sleep.

The light pressure on her mouth and the slight tickle of Geoff's beard on her chin gradually lifted her out of deep sleep and into dreamy contentment. She lifted an arm and curled it around his neck and her lips parted on a sigh of drowsy pleasure, inviting another kiss. His tongue tingled over the inner side of her lips and she met it with her own, teasing back as she langourously moved her body towards his. The pleasantly erotic play of the kiss quickly deepened, jolting her fully awake with its passionate demand.

But it wasn't Geoff kissing her! He had never kissed her like this; and Geoff was dead, dead and buried four years ago! Jackie opened her eyes, shocked out of her wits. She saw a mane of golden hair shining above her in the moonlight. Fear paralysed her into rigidity. She had read about rape but had never expected to experience it. And she couldn't even scream! That cursedly persuasive mouth was plundering hers with mounting intensity.

He had moved the top half of his body over hers, pinning one of her arms underneath him, but the one she had curled around his neck was free. She raked her fingernails down his back. She found it was strong and muscular, and he only seemed to take encouragement from the action. She kicked out with both legs. They hit nothing.

Panic drove her hand back up into his thick hair and her fingers tugged fiercely at it. The pressure on her mouth relaxed. The man slowly lifted his head, a deep sigh whispering from his still-parted lips; full, sensual lips, she noted resentfully. She could smell the alcohol on his breath. She didn't know the man. She had never seen anyone remotely like him in her entire life.

It was the beard that had fooled her in that moment between sleep and wakefulness, but it was unlike Geoff's beard. It was golden for a start, and barbered to an aggressive point. Even his eyebrows were golden, glistening above eyes that were twinkling with devilish mischief. Which suggested he couldn't be a serious rapist.

Jackie activated her vocal chords, even though they felt positively strangled. 'Who . . . who are you?'

The full lips curved whimsically as he stroked her cheek with featherlight fingertips. 'How very beautiful you are.' His voice was a soft musical croon, as enchanting as a sigh of wind through a grove of trees.

For one wildly imaginative moment Jackie fancied him as a Norse god, straight out of the myths and legends, but common sense and the reality of firm, warm flesh and blood pressing against her chest quickly dispelled that romantic notion. 'You ... you get away from me,' she snarled at him. 'Leave me alone.'

The smile widened to a gleam of white teeth. 'When you speak with so much repressed feeling, your breasts rise and gently caress my chest. Do you realise how exciting that is?'

She suddenly realised his chest was bare. And she had raked bare skin on his back. My God! Was he completely naked? 'You get off me this instant,' she squeaked, then swiftly drew breath for more vehemence. 'If you don't get off me I'll call my husband and he'll shoot you. Both barrels of a twelve-gauge shotgun.'

His soft chuckle was a musical mockery of her threat. 'Mrs Mulholland, your husband died four years ago, climbing the north face of the Matterhorn. From exposure, I believe. I also know that you're completely alone here and at my mercy,' he added teasingly.

Her thoughts winged instantly to the boys, innocently asleep at the back of the house. But she could not call out to them. She could not risk involving them if there was any danger. 'How do you know that?' she prevaricated.

'I have my sources of information,' was the blithe reply.

'Who are you?' she asked again, more insistently.

He dragged himself off her with a reluctant sigh.

Jackie scrambled to her feet and was up, her back pressed against the door-jamb in protective readiness, before he straightened to his full height, which was far too impressive for her peace of mind. The swimming trunks he wore—if that was what they were—barely covered his private parts, and the body on show was an artist's dream: a flowing line of firm flesh and muscle in perfect proportion.

He nonchalantly leaned back against the veranda railing and grinned at her. 'No cause for fight or flight. You've just had the pleasure of meeting Sunny King.'

The arrogance of the man! The sheer, blazing arrogance! Not to mention... Jackie's voice dripped ice. 'It wasn't a pleasure, Mr King. It was ...' Her mind whizzed through its stored vocabulary for a suitable put-down and she produced it with venom. '... disgusting!' Her voice rose in outrage. 'How dare you do that to me?'

He looked pained and his hand waved an appeasing gesture. 'Mrs Mulholland, you simply misread the situation. I was only practising a device I learnt on safari in South Africa. Best way of waking someone up without frightening them. Always used it on the women when lions and tigers were on the prowl.'

'Not to mention yourself, Mr King,' she snapped contemptuously. 'Don't try to sweet-talk me. I ...'

'Please call me Sunny.'

'I know precisely who you are and all you've done. I've even seen a couple of the early movies you produced ...'

'Marvellous!'

'. . . all of which were crummy!' Jackie topped him with triumphant satisfaction. 'Just because you got lucky and made a cult movie on a shoestring budget . . .'

He held up his palm. 'Say no more. I understand everything. You resent my success.'

Jackie snarled at his smug visage. '. . . don't think you can steal up on me in the middle of the night and start kissing me. Now, get the hell off my place!'

He folded his arms and nodded gravely. 'Certainly. Never stay where I'm not wanted. Sorry you don't want to be neighbourly. What do you want me to do with the boys?'

Jackie's outrage blanked into confusion. 'What boys?' Surely to God they were safely asleep in bed! There hadn't been a squeak out of either of them.

The smile on Sunny King's face was one of pleasant indifference. 'Let me see now,' he drawled. 'There's the one called Robert Falcon, after the Scott who explored the Antarctic, and the other called Edmund Percival, after the Hillary who climbed to the top of Mount Everest.'

Every maternal hackle in Jackie's body rose to the fore. 'Where are my children?' she demanded fiercely.

'We discovered them up a tree, observing our party at close range. At the present moment they are discussing abseiling with my secretary, Trevor Haines. They didn't seem terribly eager to leave, so I took it upon myself, out of the kindness of my heart, to . . .'

'I'm sorry you've been troubled with them,'

Jackie cut in stiffly. 'I'll come and bring them home.'

'No trouble. No trouble at all. Terribly fortunate. If I hadn't thought you might be worried by their absence if you happened to discover it, I wouldn't have come down. And here you were, lying in the moonlight, a picture of beauty revealed . . .'

A flood of heat ripped through Jackie's body as she remembered just how thin her cotton nightie was. 'I'll go and get dressed straight away,' she gabbled and darted into the darkness of the hallway.

'No hurry,' floated after her. 'The night is still young, the air scented with magic, the . . .'

Those damned little monkeys, Jackie seethed, throwing open their bedroom door to check that their beds were indeed empty. Which they were. And the window wide open. Just wait until she got her hands on them!

She banged into the bathroom, slapped some water on her face, and pulled a brush through her short black hair. Beauty revealed, she scoffed at herself in the mirror. Well, she supposed she didn't look too bad for a thirty-one-year-old. Her skin was still creamy smooth and her thick-lashed eyes were as good as they had always been. A tantalising hazel, Geoff used to say. And her . . . Oh, good God! What on earth was she doing, taking notice of that stupid Sunny King? She wrinkled her dainty little nose in disgust and stomped into her bedroom.

Those disobedient little brats were going to get the tongue-lashing of their lives. Here it was—she glanced at the bedside clock—almost two in the morning, and she had to trek up to that den of iniquity to collect them. And what the devil would she put on?

She threw off her nightie, grabbed a pair of briefs from her underwear drawer and dragged them on, then turned to the wardrobe, deciding any old dress would do. She was certainly not going partying at Sunny King's place.

'You know, for a woman who's had two kids, you have a fantastic body.'

She whipped around to find Sunny King propped indolently against the door-jamb, eyeing her with unashamed lechery.

'Luscious breasts. Just right,' he observed appreciatively.

Fire burned into her cheeks as temper soared to boiling point. 'You really are the end!' she snapped at him, whipping out a top and dragging it over her torso.

'I bet you'd win any wet T-shirt competition you went in,' he mused.

'Will you get out of here?' she yelled, snatching up the shorts she had let drop on to the floor last night.

'I'm patiently waiting for you. Got the car outside ready to run you down the road. I do like short shorts, particularly on a cheeky bottom.'

'Do you make a profession of being offensive?' she grated at him, slipping her feet into a pair of sandals.

'Me? Offensive?' The golden eyebrows rose into surprised peaks but his eyes were laughing at her.

Blue eyes, she noticed. Bedroom eyes, she thought as she scorned his profession of innocence. 'Assaulting defenceless women. Voyeurism. No respect for privacy ...'

'Do you begrudge me a few primitive urges?' he cut in with teasing mockery. 'That's the trouble with today's society. Too uptight. Lost touch with their basic selves. Let it all flow out, I say.'

'Well, if you don't mind, I'd like to flow down the road and collect my children,' Jackie shot at him with acid sarcasm.

His arm swept an invitation. 'At your service.'

He did not move and she was forced to brush past him. He had the gall to pat her bottom and Jackie fumed with frustration. Male chauvinist pig! Her hand itched to belt his insolent face but common sense told her that discretion was the better part of valour.

Better to get him back to his party for his fun and games; any tussle with him here could only lead to further indignities. But next time she would be ready for him, with the twelve-gauge shotgun on hand. If there ever was a next time, and please God there wouldn't be! Sunny King would never set foot on her place again if she could help it.

A long sleek sports car stood at the gate. It glinted golden, too. Just who did he think he was? The Sun-king? Had he coined his ridiculous name from the God of ancient Egypt? He was so damned full of himself.

'It's a Lagonda,' he said proudly as he opened the passenger door for her.

The car screamed wealth, luxury and perform-ance, and once Sunny King took the wheel, he let it perform. The tyres screeched as he slammed his foot on the accelerator. Jackie sagged back in the seat. Show-off, she notched up silently. It went neatly with all his other faults.

They screamed down the road. Braking heavily, Sunny King slid the car sideways to line it up with his own driveway. Then once again the fierce acceleration as he zoomed up to the house, spraying gravel everywhere with an abrupt halt in front of the triple garage.

'Nice car,' he said with a wide smile, patting the wheel benevolently as he added, 'worth about twice the price of a Rolls.'

Jackie added boastfulness to the list of vices. 'Thanks for the lift,' she said sarcastically. 'I'll get the children out of your hair and be on my way.'

'I'll drive you back.'

Jackie gritted her teeth into a semblance of a smile. 'No. Please don't do that.' Once was quite enough. She was lucky to have arrived safely and she wasn't going to risk a return trip. 'We'll walk,' she said firmly.

'Nonsense. Besides, I want you to stay a while. You haven't seen through the house and it'll give me great pleasure to show it to you. I'm very proud of it.'

Jackie added pride to the list. In an effort to be fair, she wondered if he had any virtues at all, but a moment's recollection brought none to mind. She suffered the light grasp on her arm as he led her to the house.

'It's very late,' she stated firmly.

He grinned at her, completely irrepressible. 'Just a few minutes of your time to dwell on one of the new wonders of the world.'

He threw open the double front doors. Just inside, flanking the entrance, stood two statues, copies of Greek sculpture, both nude figures. If that was not enough, the sounds of uninhibited revelry rooted Jackie's feet to the ground. Fortunately the rock band had taken a break so her voice was clearly audible as she laid down the line.

'It is late, Mr King. My children should have been in bed hours ago. I do not wish to come in. If you would please see that the boys are brought to me, we will not delay you from your guests any longer.'

He eyed the mutinous set of her face, adopted a crestfallen look for a moment, and, when that had no softening effect on her expression, shrugged his shoulders and stepped over to the balustrade which separated the mezzanine foyer from the floor below. 'Trevor!' he roared at the top of his voice.

There was a chorus of welcoming cries.

'Hey, Sunny!'

'Where've you been, man?'

'Come on down and join the party!'

Jackie watched sourly as he waved a kingly salute. His secretary came bounding up the curved staircase on the right. He was a young man, full of bright enthusiasm, eager to carry out any of his employer's whims. Jackie eyed him with increasing jaundice. Obviously a born yes-man. He gave the impression of worshipping the ground on which Sunny King walked.

'What have you done with Robert and Edmund?' the great man asked.

Jackie approved of that direct question.

Trevor Haines caught sight of her. 'Oh, Mrs Mulholland. It's all right. They're here somewhere.'

'Trevor, how come you know Mrs Mulholland?' Sunny demanded a little peevishly.

'I told you that Mrs Mulholland had called by, Sunny. Remember? And you said ...'

He waved a dismissive hand. 'You neglected to mention she was a beautiful young widow,' he said accusingly. 'You did wrong.'

'Well, I ...' His young face went a bright beet-root red as he turned to Jackie in apology.

She had to choke back a laugh. To Trevor, who was only in his early twenties, she was not young, and what beauty she had was only in the eye of the beholder. But they were straying from the business in hand. 'The boys?' she reminded him.

'Oh, they are here, Mrs Mulholland,' he quickly assured her. 'I had to deal with ... uh ... some other business, and they asked if they could look through the house, and I knew Sunny wouldn't mind, so I told them to go ahead.'

'Splendid!' his employer declared, clapping him on the back with approval. 'Nothing for you to worry about, Trevor. Mrs Mulholland and I will go and find them.' And he turned to her with smug triumph written all over his face.

So there was to be no avoiding entering the lion's den. But let him try anything! Just let him try anything more on her and he would see who had claws!

CHAPTER TWO

MAKING movies had obviously gone to Sunny King's head in a big way, Jackie decided. And so had the money he had made. The entrance to his home reminded her of the balcony at the State Theatre. Mottled Greek columns lined the staircase which curved downwards from either side of the foyer; little alcoves in the wall held more statues, all of them nude; huge chandeliers hung from the enormously tall ceiling. Pompous and pretentious. No other words for it.

As they started the descent—to the pits, Jackie privately labelled the huge entertainment-room below—Sunny King hung a hand on her shoulder and grinned down at her. 'Fit for a king, isn't it?' The pun on his own name obviously gave him a lot of satisfaction.

Jackie dropped her shoulder and stepped sideways, giving him her best look of disdain. 'It reeks of wealth, if that's any commendation.'

He chuckled, his twinkling blue gaze skating over the prominent outline of her breasts. 'True. But it has given me enormous pleasure to create one of the majestic homes of the century. The great movie actresses of the past would have given their eye-teeth to make a dramatic entrance down these steps.'

Jackie's mouth clamped into a thin line. There was no point in rising to his grandiose spiel. Clearly his hide was so thick it couldn't be punctured, no matter what she said.

'Come and I'll introduce you to some of today's stars,' he continued with unflagging enthusiasm, his hand making its way around her waist this time. 'Most of the cast from . . .'

She stopped dead. 'Mr King, I am not here to play the star-struck fan. I am here to take my children home.' She waved a dismissive hand at the crowd of guests below them. 'I don't see them down there. Do you?'

He didn't bother to look. His gaze was fixed on her uptilted face. 'Do you know there are gold flecks in your eyes? Gives them a tigerish quality. I bet you'll love the guest-room in the turret. It's just through here.'

He steered her into a passageway off the first landing and opened a door, virtually bundling her inside the room as he switched on the light. Jackie's eyes almost rolled in their sockets at the incredible décor. It was some mad cross between a sheikh's tent and a safari nightmare. Great loops of tiger-printed material fell from a high central peak, which she imagined reached to the ceiling, and draped the whole of the circular wall. The quilt on the bed featured quilted tigers and the floor had tiger-skin rugs all over it.

'What do you think?' Sunny King asked with all the eagerness of a little boy who wanted to be patted on the head.

Jackie was struck dumb.

'Knocked you speechless?' he crowed. 'Wait till you see the rest.'

Never, not in magazines, in movies, in any crazy stretch of the imagination, had Jackie seen such rampant opulence as Sunny King showed her in his guided tour. The dining-room was all blue and gold—peacock-blue with decorative jars of peacock feathers, which was certainly in character for her host. The private movie theatre was all plush red—naturally. The kitchen was surely the largest in the world and equipped with every gadget under the sun. Jackie had hoped to find the boys there, feeding their faces or guzzling free soft drink, but so such luck.

Beyond the central entertainment-room, which ended in a spectacular wall of glass, was a flagstoned terrace of tennis-court proportions, and Jackie noted that the rock band was set up out there, which explained why the music had been so loud. She winced as she saw the band members picking up their instruments once more. There were people everywhere but still no sign of Robert and Edmund. She wondered if they had sneaked back home in an attempt to avoid trouble.

Sunny King kept urging her around his dazzling domain: the games-room with its lush billiard table, mirrored bar and sunken swimming-pool; mind-boggling bathrooms with spas and saunas; bedrooms galore, each one a masterpiece of vulgar sensuality where the furnishings were concerned. There was no doubt about it, the man was nothing but a satyr.

'And finally we come to the *pièce de résistance*, the master bedroom,' Sunny King purred in her ear, and opened the door with a flourish.

Jackie came to an abrupt halt in the doorway. Her eyes glazed as they took in the massive four-poster bed with its golden gauze curtaining. The walls featured the more pornographic paintings of Norman Lindsay. The ceiling was painted like the Sistine Chapel, except the theme was certainly not heavenly.

'Wish I could have got Michelangelo to do that, but apparently he's dead,' Sunny King said with a cheerfully lascivious grin. 'However, the carving on the bedhead is marvellous. Inspirational. It came from Bali.'

He moved across the room to sweep the nearest curtain aside. He waved an invitation to her. 'Have a look! It's incredibly clever how everything intertwines. Master craftsmen.'

Jackie could imagine what was intertwined and she wasn't budging a foot inside this sybarite's bedroom.

'Don't be shy,' he urged. 'You'll like it.'

She had seen more than enough and the boys had obviously skipped out somewhere along the line. 'Do you really want my opinion, Mr King?' she asked silkily.

'Sunny,' he corrected her with a confident smile. 'And yes, I would like your opinion.'

'I think it's dreadful,' she said with lofty disdain.

The smile faltered and slowly curled into something else as he strolled back to her. 'So I can't impress you, Mrs Mulholland?'

She sensed danger but recklessly defied it. 'Not a ghost of a chance, Mr King.'

'Is that right? Then you shouldn't be standing under the mistletoe.'

Jackie glanced up in disbelief and that momentary reaction was her undoing. Before she could strike a defensive stance, Sunny King was holding her and kissing her again. She tried to struggle against his embrace but that didn't work. His arms were too strong and he moved in closer, his thighs pressing against hers. Not just pressing but rubbing in a sensual manner that made her electrically aware of the silken down on his legs. For one awful moment she felt her own thighs quiver in . . . in pleasure?

Alarm bells went off in Jackie's head. Passive resistance had to be employed. Sunny King's mountainous ego wouldn't like that and he would soon get tired of trying to wring blood out of a stone. Be as still and as cold as his damned statues, she told herself. A few moments were enough to convince her that passive resistance didn't work.

His mouth played over hers with tantalising persuasiveness, and he took advantage of the lack of resistance to slide his hands down the curve of her spine and curl them around her bottom. His body swayed erotically against hers. No crude thrusting. Oh no! A provocative teasing that built anticipation to an explosive need to clutch him to her, hold him fast, grind her own body into his.

Her whole nervous system was going haywire, sending a chaotic mass of urgent messages to her brain. Melt! Give in! Take him! Forget everything else! Only this matters now! Now, now, now!

Sanity fought back. Sunny King was a vain, proud prig of a man who thought he could sweep her off her feet, and was obviously intent on doing so. He had arrogantly taken advantage of her, as he undoubtedly did with any woman who crossed his lecherous path. To let him have her as another conquest was unthinkable. Totally unacceptable.

But it had been so long since she had been aroused like this, so long since such excitement had been swarming through her veins ... her whole body pulsing with ...

Jackie ruthlessly crushed the treacherous wail of thought. Not Sunny King, pride insisted. Never him! She slid her hands up to his shoulders, meaning to lever herself away. He chose that moment to clamp her lower body to his and all stomach for resistance collapsed. She gasped as desire shot through her in a gathering spiral of heat that plastered her to him in weak abandonment. His mouth seduced hers with an erotic invasion that scrambled any possibility of rational thought. She responded with wild, mindless passion.

Some four metres away, underneath the king-size four-poster bed, Edmund wriggled over to Robert and tapped his shoulder. 'Do you think they're gone?' he whispered.

Robert frowned his uncertainty. 'Don't know.'

Edmund rolled his eyes. 'We're going to cop it. That was Mum and she didn't sound happy.'

'She's mad as hell, I reckon.'

There was a moment of mournful silence while they contemplated their prospective fates. 'It was worth it anyway,' Robert decided.

'Yeah,' his younger brother agreed. Edmund's persistently inquisitive mind pulled out a curious remark. 'I didn't see any mistletoe.'

'Me neither. I'm going to take a peek.'

With all the guile of twelve-year-old deviousness, he slithered to the corner of the bed where the gold brocade valance was slit to fit around the corner-post. With his face pressed hard to the carpet he lifted the flap far enough to get a sight of the floor between him and the doorway. The vision of two pairs of feet toe to toe, one set of which were encased in his mother's sandals, absolutely intrigued him. He poked his head out a little further. Edmund wriggled up beside him to see for himself. They looked at one another in startled wonder and ducked back behind the valance.

'Mum's kissing Sunny King!' Edmund's whispered voice carried a peculiar note of awe.

'They're just about glued together,' Robert agreed, even more awed.

Caution was swept aside by a novelty too great to be missed. Both heads poked out from under the bed, eyes agog with fascinated interest.

Sunny King chose that particular moment to

lift Jackie off her feet—only far enough to serve the dual purpose of fitting her pliant softness to a more intimate nicety with his own increasingly urgent need, and allowing him to move her to the bed without any awkwardness. Her arms wound more tightly around his neck, instinctively abetting the desire that was rampaging through both of them. His mouth left hers with a sigh of deep satisfaction and her long graceful throat bent to the sensual play of his lips as he turned to take the few necessary steps.

Jackie opened eyes that were carelessly sightless, until they met other eyes. Shock jack-knifed her limp body into violent rejection. 'Edmund!' she squeaked; then, in mounting horror, 'Robert!'

Her hands beat reflexively on Sunny King's broad shouders. 'Let me go! The boys ... Edmund! Robert! You come out here this instant!'

Sunny King took another step towards the bed.

'Let me go!' she shrieked. 'The boys are under the bed.'

That stopped him but he did not release her.

She clenched her hands into fists and banged them down on his shoulders in frustration, all desire raging into panic-stricken anger. How could she have been so weak as to succumb to Sunny King's seductive manoeuvres! And the boys had been watching them! For how long? All the time that she had been swept along in that whirlpool of passion?

'Put me down!' she commanded in shrill desperation.

Sunny King ignored her.

Jackie wriggled frantically against his hold. 'Robert and Edmund, get yourselves out here at once!' she cried, almost reduced to appealing for their help in freeing her from this terrible man.

She caught only a glimpse of their crawling bodies before Sunny King lowered her enough to smother her mouth with another kiss. She tried to heave herself away but to no avail. He had her head clamped to his with one immovable hand. She clutched his mane of hair and pulled with furious might.

'Beast!' she hissed at him as he finally freed her lips.

'Didn't you like it, Mum?' Edmund's voice held a note of disappointed curiosity.

'Certainly not!' she snapped, pushing angrily against the seemingly impervious strength of Sunny King's embrace. She glared at him, furious with herself for having momentarily fallen victim to his sexual expertise. 'You are the most depraved, disgusting man I've ever met. Now let me go!'

'Only when you tell the truth. Admit you enjoyed every minute of it.'

Still he held her pinned to him in flaunting intimacy. In front of her own children! She felt utterly humiliated. His arrogant disregard for her feelings spurred a wild rage. She beat at him with flailing fists, but that didn't seem to make any impression on him. He ducked and weaved his head, an insidious smile on his face.

She lifted back one dangling foot and kicked his shin as hard as she could. He only blinked. And kept smiling at her. Jackie felt as though she had broken a toe. 'Let me go!' she shrilled at him. 'You ... you ... troglodyte!'

'What's that mean?' he asked in mystification.

'Look it up in a dictionary, you ignoramus.'

He laughed, a soft mocking laugh that sent a tormenting tingle down her spine. Then very gently he placed her on her feet and released her. 'Do you feel better now?'

Her cheeks burned with shame as he made a covert adjustment to his swimming trunks, and then she stepped away, trembling with outrage. 'I won't feel better until I'm out of this ... this palace of perversion.'

His laughter goaded her into violent reaction. She wheeled on Robert and Edmund, grabbed their arms and marched them out of the room.

'I don't think it will be long before you're back, Mrs Mulholland.'

The cynical amusement in Sunny King's musical voice spurred a fierce determination never to have anything to do with him again. Not for any reason. Jackie hauled the boys into a faster stride. They practically had to trot to keep up with her. She barely drew breath until they were out of the house.

Robert and Edmund exchanged eye-signals as their mother plunged them all down the driveway to the road. Silence was definitely indicated. The state of temper was uncertain and now was not the time for pleading mitigating circumstances for their escapade.

For the whole two hundred metres or so up the road to their adjoining property, they trailed cautiously in her wake. When they reached the gateway and the house was only another thirty metres away, Robert felt it was time to try some mollifying tactic.

'You sure are a good fighter, Mum,' he said admiringly.

'She's not as good as Sunny King,' Edmund blurted out, earning a venomous look from his brother.

'Do not refer to me as she,' Jackie grated. 'I am not the cat's mother.' She glared at both of them. 'And the name of Sunny King is not to be spoken in front of me again.'

'Yes, Mum,' Robert agreed with alacrity, very relieved by this amazing decision of his mother's. How could she lecture them if Sunny King was not to be mentioned?

'Why not?' Edmund asked.

The stupid dope, Robert thought in exasperation, shaking his head at his younger brother behind his mother's back. Although Edmund was only fifteen months younger than himself, sometimes he acted like a thick-headed little kid. It was perfectly obvious that Sunny King had somehow got the better of their mother and she was mad as hell about it. Even madder about that than she was about their sneaking off.

'That man can only be a bad influence. You are never to step foot on his property again,' came the vehement edict.

By this time they had reached the front steps of the house. 'Now!' their mother snapped. 'Get off to bed. Both of you. And God help you if you move out of your room again tonight.'

She let them go and Robert gave Edmund a quick shove into the hallway to save any further gaffes on his part. 'Goodnight, Mum,' they chorused with careful respect.

More like good morning, Jackie thought sourly as she bent to drag the spare mattress back inside. The pillow rolled off it as she gave an exasperated yank to get the bedding through the doorway. She bit down on an irritable curse and completed the task of pushing the mattress into the hall cupboard before going back to retrieve the pillow.

The house was still airless. Still hot. She thought of the air-conditioned coolness of Sunny King's residence and felt a sharp stab of envy. She picked up the pillow. Her body was still jangling from the sexual arousal that had been so abruptly terminated. She hugged the pillow to her in a need for soft comfort and wandered slowly around to the veranda which faced Sunny King's property.

The rock band was blaring again, the lights undimmed, the party still in full swing. A brief, titillating encounter, that was all it had been. Damn him! Damn him for using her like that! She felt terrible. Apart from the dreadful indignity of having been sprung by her children in the thrall of sexual excitement, she was now suffering the pangs of sexual frustration.

It had been years since she had felt anything like the feverish urgency he had made her feel. She had successfully managed to repress all that ever since Geoff had died, and even in the last few years before her widowhood. It had been nice, but not exactly frantic. Really, she hadn't experienced such quivering expectancy since ... since before Robert was born. In the latter years of her marriage ... Well, the plain truth was, Geoff had never been so provocatively sexy as Sunny King.

But she had loved Geoff. And she certainly didn't love that egomaniac, Sunny King. Furthermore, she wasn't going to have anything to do with him. She didn't need sex so much that she had to stoop to the likes of him for a tumble in bed. That was all it would be. He'd probably done it to a thousand women.

There were other, better men around than him if she wanted a lover. Men who would value her as a person and not just a convenient body. She hadn't really been looking for anyone since Geoff's death, but maybe she should. The boys wouldn't be with her for ever. If Sunny King found her attractive, then surely she could attract someone more compatible, someone who would be happy to share the rest of her life. Everything, not just bed!

She gritted her teeth in disgust at her unwarranted response to Sunny King and turned away to go back to her bedroom. Sleep was the immediate answer to the feeling that dreadful man had stirred. Tomorrow she would feel on top of herself again. One thing was certain: she was never going to let Sunny King get to her, not in any way whatsoever.

CHAPTER THREE

IT was late Sunday afternoon before the exodus began from Sunny King's property. First the rock band in a gaily painted camper van; then, at intermittent intervals, two Jaguars, three Mercedes, four other camper vans, one Alfa Romeo, one Lamborghini, five rather insignificant station wagons, two Volvos and the rest of the list floated over Jackie's determined indifference, although Robert and Edmund persisted in keeping her informed. The highlight of the afternoon was the arrival and departure of a helicopter.

The party was over, which was the only welcome fact as far as Jackie was concerned. She felt like something the cat had dragged in and she desperately needed a good night's sleep. A cool change had come in from the south and apart from the occasional roar of a passing vehicle—did all Sunny King's friends have a passion for mad acceleration?—blessed silence had once again returned to the countryside.

On Monday morning she even awoke to the twittering of birds. She smiled, and it was the first smile to relax her taut facial muscles for over forty-eight hours. Everything was back to normal. Almost. She had been made too aware of unfulfilled needs to forget them in a hurry, but today she would get back to working on the clay in her pottery shed; a bit of pummelling would surely work off some of her inner frustration.

If only Sunny King had not bought the property next door! He was undoubtedly going to become a continual irritant, upsetting the contented tenor of her life. For all of ten years she had been happy here. Reasonably happy, she amended, not forgetting her horror and grief over Geoff's death. She certainly had no wish to go anywhere else or do anything other than what she was doing.

Which was something her parents had never understood, Jackie thought ruefully, remembering their disapproval at her lack of ambition. She did appreciate the broad and expensive education they had given her, and she had done very well at school, but somehow the continual living up to her parents' expectations had gradually palled, particularly since there had never been any time for other things.

Her parents had been so devoted to their own careers, Jackie had often wondered if she had been a mistake. Her mother had been thirty-seven at the time of Jackie's birth and really her parents had seemed to resent her intrusion into their lives. Certainly she had not felt important to them.

Not like with Geoff. He had shown her what love was all about. Geoff had cared about her feelings and had always made her feel valued as a person. She had never regretted her marriage to him. It did not matter that she had not gone on to art college, anyway. She had done quite well with her pottery without further tuition. And she always had time for her children. It was a good life that she had.

Except for missing Geoff.

But if Sunny King thought that her being a widow made her an easy prey, she would soon make him think again! That lecherous movie-mogul might have the golden touch but she could see his feet of clay. Clay . . . A smile of wicked satisfaction grew on Jackie's face as an inspired idea floated into her mind. Her pottery line of prehistoric animals was selling particularly well, but she was sick of doing dinosaurs. She would create something new, sort of like a llama with Sunny King's face on it. Definitely prehistoric.

The smile widened into a grin. She would fire it in the old brick-kiln behind the shed. Electricity wouldn't do for Sunny King. Definitely a wood fire, stoked to an absolute blaze of heat. It would be as good as burning an effigy.

Robert and Edmund were pleased to see their mother's easy-going humour restored. She was humming happily to herself as she worked on her clay and didn't even ask why they wanted the old sheets of galvanised iron from under the veranda. They were almost away scot-free when she commented absently, 'It's not another tree-house, is it?'

'No, Mum,' they assured her quickly, and raced off to begin building their canoe.

They all had a very satisfying few days without a ripple of disturbance on the home front. In fact, by Wednesday night Jackie had completely recovered her equanimity. Until the telephone rang and Sunny King's distinctive voice came over the line.

'I'm free tonight,' he said cheerfully.

Well, bully for you, Jackie thought sourly as she fought to retain her hard-won equanimity. 'Are they letting you out of your cage?' she drawled with sweet indulgence.

He chuckled. 'Don't you want to see me?'

She did her best to project airy indifference. 'No. Never again, thank you.'

'Ah, that's cruel to both of us. Why don't you face up to yourself and confess that we were made for each other? Come on over. Let's do something excitingly constructive. I can feel the surge of creativity in my veins. I know you're going to stir me to . . .'

'No!' He was not going to stir her that way. She was not going to let him.

'Why not?' he asked reasonably.

'Because I couldn't stand what comes after it's finished.'

'What do you think is going to happen?'

'Once it was all over I'd be bored out of my mind. There is nothing more distressing than having had sex with someone who shares nothing else with you. You very quickly realise what a great mistake you've made. That's precisely what would happen with us.'

'How do you know that?' he asked, his voice accusing her of unwarranted fabrication.

'I read the divorce statistics.'

'I share a great deal with you. You give me a lot. There's not a chance that I'd be bored with you,' he argued.

She smiled, knowing that she had the drop on him for once. 'I know that. The problem is all on my side. I simply couldn't cope with you.'

There were several moments' silence before he admitted defeat. 'You are a first-class bitch, Mrs Mulholland,' he said cheerfully.

'No, I'm not, Mr King, but I can give a wonderful imitation of one when I put my mind to it.' And on that sweetly triumphant line she hung up on him.

However, Jackie's satisfaction frayed a little around the edges as she lay awake in her virtuous bed that night. She couldn't help wondering just how creative Sunny King might have been. Which disturbed her rather a lot, even though she was absolutely certain she had made the right decision. She pounded the clay considerably harder the next day.

A week went by, marked only by a fair increase in Jackie's potteryware and the great canoe disaster. The boys came trailing up from the river, their clothes dripping wet and their faces glum.

Jackie elicited the facts. They drove her to an exasperated outburst. 'How could you expect a canoe made out of galvanised iron to float?'

'Steel ships float,' Robert argued.

'It worked for a while,' Edmund added plaintively. 'We plugged up all the nail-holes with your modelling plasticine.'

This provocative revelation earned a daggers look from his elder brother.

Jackie sighed. Don't repress their spirit of adventure, Geoff had always said; boys will be boys. If they managed to grow up at all, they would most likely end up dying on the Matterhorn like their father, she thought dispiritedly, but nothing she said was going to change them. It was obviously in the blood.

And there were still another two weeks of the school holidays to get through. She prayed it would be without serious mishap. Perhaps they needed a spot of civilised culture to divert their minds from the more dangerous undertakings that seemed to attract them.

'We'll go to Parramatta tomorrow,' she decided brightly. 'You can go to the movies while I deliver my pottery and do some shopping.'

Robert's face lit with joy. 'Great, Mum! We've been dying to see *Live By The Sword*.'

'Yeah!' Edmund breathed ecstatically.

Jackie rolled her eyes in despair. She should have known better. It was bad enough that *Live By The Sword* was reported to be action-packed with gory violence, it was also the red-hot box office sequel to Sunny King's big hit, *Eye For An Eye*, which the boys had re-enacted in dangerous games ever since they had seen it three years ago. Another battery charge of Sunny King's one-eyed hero, Dirk Vescum, would probably result in two one-eyed children.

She tried. 'Wouldn't you like to see a comedy?'

They groaned. They argued. They invited her to go along with them and see for herself that there wasn't any harm in it. She couldn't win. Forbidding them to go would only earn their resentment, particularly since the movie had been rated for general exhibition. Every other kid from school would have seen it over the holidays. Jackie resigned herself to the inevitable, but a number of malevolent thoughts went winging their way to the property next door.

So much for civilised culture, she thought bitterly as she dropped the boys at the Village Cinema the next morning, but she cheered up considerably when the gift-shop agent raved over her Sunny King llamas. He wrote her out a lovely fat cheque, and, in a frivolous mood, Jackie bought herself a new sundress.

The boys' faces were still glowing with excitement when she picked them up and took them to Kentucky Fried Chicken for a late lunch. 'It was fantastic, Mum!' Edmund bubbled. 'You should have seen the part where Dirk Vescum cut their heads off.'

'I don't want to hear about it,' she said hurriedly.

'But it was only justice, Mum,' Robert pleaded. 'They deserved to be executed. They'd been torturing . . .'

'Robert! I said I don't want to hear about it!' Violence was totally repugnant to Jackie.

The boys bolted down their lunch and huddled together in the back seat of the car on the way home, whispering over the exploits of Dirk Vescum. Having excluded herself from the distasteful conversation, Jackie resented the fact that Sunny King had created anything that held her sons so enthralled. Him and his creativity! He couldn't lift his mind above the physical.

She was quite glad to reach Wiseman's Ferry and get out of the car while the punt took them across the river. The scenic beauty of the upper reaches of the Hawkesbury River always soothed her spirits: the lush river flats and the calm stretch of water, the thickly forested slopes rising behind them. Who would ever want to live in the city? she thought contentedly, as she breathed in the clean, fresh air.

The ferry ground to a halt and she climbed back into the car. She always enjoyed the drive to St Alban's even though the road was narrow and winding. One section of it was being resurfaced and there were signs up: PLEASE DRIVE SLOWLY, BEWARE OF WINDSCREEN DAMAGE. Jackie never drove at anything but a sedate pace, but she still automatically slowed down.

The car which zoomed past her was barely a blur, going at a faster speed than Toad of Toad Hall would ever have driven. Jackie heard it but she didn't get a chance to see it. With an almighty crack her windscreen shattered into thousands of crazed angles and she couldn't see anything at all. With her heart in her mouth she stamped her foot on the brake. The car came to a halt without hitting anything and she slumped over the wheel in relief.

'Wow! That was Sunny King's Lagonda. Can't he drive!' Edmund's voice was full of admiration.

'Anyone who had a car like that could drive as fast,' Robert observed scornfully.

Sunny King! He had done this to her! Jackie slammed out of the car, found a large stone and used it to punch a hole in the windscreen. The towering indignation she felt was compounded by her own children's feckless attitudes. Not even taking her side against that . . . that maniac! And all the money she had got from selling her work would go into replacing the windscreen. A hard, cold wrath rose inside her. Sunny King would pay for this, even if she had to hoist a stone through the windscreen of his precious Lagonda herself.

'I think Mum's mad,' Robert muttered to his younger brother as she flounced back into the car, her hand still curled around the stone she had been forced to use on her own car.

'Yeah,' Edmund breathed cautiously.

It was one of the world's greatest understatements. Driving with the broken windscreen was a nightmare; the rush of air against her face brought tears to her eyes. She fingered the rock she had placed beside her on the passenger seat. Sunny King was going to rue the way he had driven his car today.

By the time she reached his gateway, Jackie's anger was at an all-time high. Volcanic. The man represented everything she hated most. She stopped in front of his triple garage and alighted, the instrument of revenge in her hand. The garage doors were locked, unbudgeable, but Jackie was not to be defeated.

'You two boys stay in the car until I settle this business,' she ordered.

'This is really going to be something,' she heard Robert say gleefully.

But Jackie was already on her way, marching up to the front door of the house. She pressed her thumb on the door chimes and left it there. The door opened and Trevor Haines tried a welcome. 'Why, Mrs Mulholland . . .'

'Get Mr Sunny King instantly.' Her tone of

voice dispensed with welcome.

'Uh, yes, Mrs Mulholland. Please wait here.' He swung away hastily.

Jackie didn't trust him. She wouldn't trust any of Sunny King's minions in a fit. She stepped forward into the foyer, snarling at the nude Greek statues as she did so. She saw Sunny King emerge from the second turret room, which was his study. He actually hummed a song as he jogged up the stairs towards her. His arms opened wide in welcome and an inane grin cut through his beard.

'Ah, Mrs Mulholland, how pleasant of you to drop in ...'

Her eyes beamed murder back at him. 'I've come for you.'

The grin widened. 'I knew you would. And I want to talk to you.'

'Take me to your garage.' The words were seethed through gritted teeth.

He blithely ignored them. 'The neglect you have shown over our common fence in recent years is deplorable.'

'I'll give you an *Eye For An Eye* ...'

He cocked his head on one side in mild consideration. 'Really, you're looking quite distressed. What's the matter?'

She weighed the stone in her hand with grim satisfaction. 'You're going to pay for what you did with your own brand of justice, Mr King. *Live By The Sword*, die by the ...'

'Are you threatening me?'

The lilting surprise in his voice fired the

explosion. 'Yes, I am! I'm going to give you back everything . . .'

He moved so quickly she had no time to strike at him or take any evasive action as he closed in on her. Her hand with the stone was pressed behind her back and her body imprisoned by a strong arm that held her against him like a vice. To her utter bewilderment he immediately started kissing her hair and forehead and uttering soft, soothing words.

'There, there, now. There's nothing that can't be sorted out. Given time. All we need is the right kind of communication. I know . . .'

'Don't do that to me!' she squawked in vehement frustration.

'I have to. It's the only way I can get you to talk sense.'

She was up against a bare chest. Bare thighs. He only had on a skimpy pair of shorts. Didn't he ever wear proper clothes?

'See? It's working, isn't it?' he crooned, his mouth working down to her nose. 'Let me kiss you properly.'

'I can't talk at all then,' she snapped furiously.

'Exactly.'

'I'll kill you,' she muttered, ducking her head low.

His mouth moved to her ear. 'Dear Mrs Mulholland, you've entranced me from the first moment I laid eyes on you. There's a certain charm, probably a backwardness in behaviour, that I find quite enchanting . . .' He nibbled at her ear-lobe.

'You . . . you swine!'

'Combined with a marvellous vocabulary. Please let me help you. Pour your troubled soul out and I'll give it balm. Lift your head. Let me take away the pain. I'll kiss you as you should be kissed. With reverence. With passion. With . . .'

He didn't mean a word of it. He was toying with her. Hatred for all he had done to her, what he was doing to her now, burnt up her throat and burst into spitting accusation. 'Your irresponsible driving could have killed us. Killed my children. You broke my windscreen and I'm going to break *your* damned windscreen if it's the last thing I do! That might teach you that the road doesn't belong entirely to you, you . . .'

'I did that?' He let her go and stepped back a pace in astonishment.

'Yes, you did!'

His face was a picture of concern. He took her hand. 'Show me the damage.'

She wrenched her hand out of his and strode to his front door, pointing a quivering finger at her car. 'See? That's what you did!'

He obligingly followed and shook his head over the catastrophe. 'Oh dear!' His arm went comfortingly around her shoulders. 'You should always have laminated windscreens, my sweet. So dangerous not to have them.'

That was it! That was the last straw! Jackie's mind blew. Screeching like a banshee she swung her arm around, stone at the ready. Some last vestige of sanity prevented her from smashing it into his face. She wheeled and attacked the male nude statue, using her weapon like a sledge-hammer. The plaster cast crumbled under the attack.

'That's for starters,' she cried, swinging back to Sunny King, her eyes ablaze and her chest heaving from violent exertion. 'Now for the Lagonda!'

He stared at her, seemingly mesmerised by her fury for a brief instant. Then he was solemnly agreeing with her. 'You're quite right. So you should. I'll take you down to the garage. Come this way please.'

He led off down the curved staircase and, after a moment's startled pause, Jackie followed him. They went through the house, Sunny King gravely waving her on whenever she hesitated. He opened a door and stood back to usher her courteously into the triple garage.

Jackie sidled through the doorway, almost stumbling down the couple of steps to the garage floor in her anxiety to keep a reasonable distance between them, too suspicious of this placid accep-tance of Sunny King's to turn her back on him.

There's the Lagonda,' he nodded.

She backed a few paces away from him, then turned quickly. And there it was, right in front of her, the aerodynamic wedge shape so sleekly stylish, so beautifully proportioned, dazzling in its futuristic sophistication. She darted a wary glance back at the man behind her.

Sunny King sat on the step. 'Go ahead,' he invited.

Confusion weakened her rage. Why was he doing this? What game was he playing at? Somehow the initiative had slipped away from her, which wasn't fair. She worked hard on bolstering her fury. It was justified.

She strode around to the other side of the Lagonda, making sure that Sunny King couldn't play some last-minute trick on her. She balanced the stone in her grip, raised her arm. Doubts rocketed around her mind. She couldn't do it. It was wrong.

Her gaze wavered back to Sunny King. 'You really want me to do this to your car?' she asked hesitantly.

He made an open-handed gesture. 'If it makes you feel better.'

Jackie's brain whirled in dismay. How was she going to get out of this predicament with her pride intact? She looked at the fancy tinted winscreen of the Lagonda, fiercely reminding herself of the damage done to her own. Determination poised her arm to strike again, but she still couldn't do it. She glared at Sunny King, resenting his crazy passivity.

'No one else in the world would let me do this,' she shot at him in bitter accusation.

He shrugged. 'I'm not the same as anyone else.'

It was no use. She couldn't carry on with it. All the pent-up ferocity had drained out of her. She lowered her arm and, with a sigh of disgust at herself, dropped the stone on the floor. He had beaten her. Again! But a spark of fiery defiance rose from the ashes of defeat. She lifted her chin and met Sunny King's gaze with stubborn pride.

'I can't do it. It's wrong. Even so, I did you a favour over that statue. It was a crass piece of pseudo-art. And anyway, you started it, driving in a mad, reckless, irresponsible fashion. It's only because I cannot wittingly destroy something of real value that I'm not paying you back what you deserve.'

He nodded and stood up. 'I'll pay for your new windscreen. In fact . . .' He turned and shouted down the hallway. 'Trevor! Come down here please!'

The secretary came running.

'Trevor, I've inadvertently given Mrs Mulholland a great deal of distress. My fault. Please take her car, get a new windscreen installed, and pay for it.'

'Sure, Sunny.'

'And give her the keys to the Daimler. She'll need a car while her own is being repaired.'

'Right.'

'No, I . . . I can't,' Jackie protested, appalled by the generosity of what was being offered her, particularly in the wake of her own vengeful rage.

He swung his gaze to her. 'I insist.' Then he smiled as though happily struck with an idea that pleased him. 'Besides, I need your advice on a new statue.'

Shame crawled down her spine. She should never have lost her temper like that. There was no excuse for such wanton destruction. That act alone dismissed any debt that Sunny King owed her. She took a deep breath to counter the sick feeling growing inside her and shook her head at him. 'No . . . no, you can't . . . I won't . . .'

'Yes,' he said firmly. 'Trevor, the keys.'

The secretary rummaged in a drawer, found the

set he was looking for and brought them over to
Jackie, thrusting them into her hand. 'There you
are, Mrs Mulholland.'

'No. I . . .' He had turned away before she could
thrust them back. She felt stupidly helpless, robbed
of all resolve. Sunny King was doing it again,
taking all control out of her hands. Not letting her
have any say in the matter.

He started strolling towards her. 'Trevor, if
you'd go and fetch Robert and Edmund down here,
I'll look after Mrs Mulholland and show her how to
drive the car.'

The secretary obeyed him without question,
leaving Jackie alone in the garage with Sunny King
who opened the driver's door of the Daimler and
took up a casual stance by it.

'Please sit inside so I can familiarise you with the
controls,' he invited pleasantly.

Jackie tried once again to make an independent
stand. 'I really don't want . . .'

'If you don't get in, I'll pick you up and put you
in,' he continued just as pleasantly.

Mutiny stirred, stiffening her backbone. But one
look at the quirky little smile on Sunny King's face
reminded her that mutiny had not served her well
in dealing with him. It was either surrender her
pride or be subjected to further indignities, since he
had the advantage on her where physical strength
was concerned. She moved towards the car,
watching him warily. 'Promise not to touch me,'
she insisted.

'For the moment,' he agreed, devilment dancing
into the blue eyes.

She didn't trust him. Couldn't trust him. She quickly slid into the driver's seat and he shut the door on her, grinning openly as he rounded the bonnet to the passenger's side. Jackie stared at the polished walnut dashboard. How could she possibly accept the loan of a Daimler in place of her six-year-old Datsun? On the other hand, how could she get out of it when Sunny King had no scruples about pressuring her with physical blackmail?

He settled in beside her and slid an arm around her shoulders. Her pulse gave a panicky leap. Her eyes flew to his in mute protest but the laughing mischief that looked back at her was mesmerising in its sexy invitation.

'You promised not to touch me,' she half choked, her breath catching in her throat at his threatening nearness.

A hand came down on her thigh. 'The temptation was too great, and I want you to be happy.' The hand was caressing her thigh. His face was coming closer.

She didn't know whether to grab his hand away or push his head back. She just couldn't cope with Sunny King's aggressive tactics at all. 'Don't kiss me,' she cried, suddenly deciding the hand was the more disturbing factor.

'Of course not.' He lifted the offending hand out of her scrabbling grasp. 'I was just going to show you how to fix the seat belt. But now that you mention it . . .'

The hand curved around her face, tilting it as his mouth came down to take possession of hers. He was doing it to her again, kissing her so damned persuasively that she didn't want to fight it. The feelings he was arousing were entirely sensual, sexual, all very physical. She couldn't possibly like the man. But he certainly was an expert at what he was doing.

She was co-operating in her own defeat, her mind told her plaintively. It told her to lift her free hand up to his shoulder and do something about it, since she was too weak to tear her mouth away from his. She lifted her hand, and his shoulder was smooth and round and nice to feel, and her hand slithered up, trying out a new course of its own.

His gentle hold on her face turned into a downward caress that found her breast, traced around it, did soft, pleasurable things to the tender fullness of it. She shouldn't allow it. She really shouldn't, Jackie's mind chided, but it did give her such a lovely melting feeling.

The noise of the children coming down the hallway jolted her out of the seductive spell he was weaving through her defences. Her eyes flew open in an urgent plea for discretion because she felt ridiculously helpless, her lips still throbbing with sensitivity, her body crying out for his touch. It was madness. He was a sex maniac on the loose. If he kept this up, there would come a time when she wanted his lovemaking, might even come to expect it.

He moved back, his hand dropping on to her thigh again, but only to give it a reassuring squeeze before it quickly withdrew. 'You're accustomed to driving automatic, aren't you?' he questioned in a casual voice, as if nothing at all had happened.

She looked dazedly at the gear lever. 'Yes,' she whispered, her voice as tattered as her defences.

The boys burst into the garage. 'Mum, are we really going to have the Daimler?'

'Yes,' Sunny King said emphatically.

Jackie felt hopelessly flustered, her eyes lifting to his in panicky appeal. 'Not really. If I hit anything . . .'

He smiled. 'Consider your revenge complete.'

The man was impossible. She tried to think of other arguments, but Sunny King was telling the kids to pile into the back seat and Trevor Haines was passing over her handbag and handing the boys her shopping. She was not in control at all, and it didn't seem she ever would be around Sunny King. How could such an overbearing, abominable man reduce her to such . . . such quivering jelly?

The boys hung over the front seats, excited and fascinated as Sunny King explained how the thermostat of the air-conditioning system worked, and the radio-cassette-player, and the hand brake and the alarm system. Jackie could hardly take it all in. She felt relieved when Sunny King got out to open the garage door, but felt too nervous to start the car. He came back to her window and smiled at her.

'Just turn the key in the ignition and put the gear into drive. No problem,' he assured her. 'And I'll see you tonight.'

'No.' She shook her head vehemently.

'Aw, come on, Mum,' Robert urged, not understanding.

Sunny King's smile tilted appealingly. 'About

the fences. Something's got to be done about them. They're an eyesore.'

'No,' she repeated more sharply, desperate to keep him at a distance until she had sorted herself out. 'If you want something done about the fence, do it yourself.' She started the engine to punctuate the point.

He patted her shoulder. 'We'll discuss it tonight. Bye now.'

The boys chorused back happy farewells and Jackie drove out of the garage with a sinking feeling of utter defeat. Somewhere along the line she had lost the argument, lost her common sense, lost all direction. How on earth was she going to handle Sunny King tonight? She couldn't even handle herself!

CHAPTER FOUR

'MUM, can we go abseiling with Trevor Haines?'
Robert asked eagerly, breaking into Jackie's agitated concentration over driving Sunny King's Daimler.

It took her a couple of seconds to register the question, then her mind instantly ballooned with horror. 'No, you certainly cannot!'

'Why not?' Edmund demanded plaintively.

'You're not old enough,' Jackie snapped. 'I told you that before.'

'Dad did it at our age,' Robert pointed out reasonably.

'No! The answer is no!' Jackie repeated with a vehemence that didn't allow any leeway for argument.

Her emotions were all achurn as it was, and here her children were, reminding her of Geoff's death. The memory of that loss bit deep. Geoff, the adventurer, the man to whom nothing was impossible, who wanted to experience everything that would make any normal person flinch in fear. And their children hero-worshipped his image, his memory. It was terribly worrying, more worring than anything Sunny King could do to her.

On the other hand, both boys idolised Dirk Vescum, the fantasy hero of Sunny King's movies.

And this handsome gesture of lending them a Daimler ... it was sure to make the boys think Sunny King was marvellous too. She shouldn't have taken it. She shouldn't have responded to his kiss. She shouldn't have done a lot of things. It was very unsettling to find herself so vulnerable to a man like Sunny King.

She drove the Daimler into the old shed that served as a garage and felt slightly calmer as she successfully brought it to a halt without mishap. It was just plain stupid her having this car at all. She didn't need it; her own would surely be repaired by tomorrow afternoon. She would make Sunny King take it back tonight—it was too big a favour for her to accept. Perhaps he was expecting it to buy her favour. Wasn't that the type of tactic movie moguls used to woo their women?

Jackie was out of the luxury car as fast as a scalded cat. She hurried into the sanctuary of her own home, telling herself she would never, never, never stoop to becoming one of Sunny King's women. Even if he was a handsome devil with sex appeal galore, she had had plenty of evidence about his character and that was all bad. There was no doubt that there had to be a devious motive behind his generosity. Any involvement with Sunny King could only bring her grief.

Jackie sighed in irritation as she noticed that the house was in a mess. Too many hours spent in the pottery shed, she berated herself, although she had to acknowledge that she wasn't the greatest housekeeper in the world at the best of times. The boys only compounded the problem, leaving things lying around if she didn't hound them. In a tone of voice that brooked no excuses, she ordered a general clean-up.

She wasn't doing this for Sunny King, Jackie told herself. It didn't matter what he thought of her home. It didn't matter what he thought of her either. It was simply a matter of pride and self-respect that she made the living-room as tidy as possible. Then, having finished with the evening meal, she felt constrained to give the kitchen a thorough cleaning.

However, all the scrubbing in the world couldn't scrub out her concern over having to face Sunny King again. He always seemed to turn the tables on her in the most disconcerting manner. Her concern grew into resentment. It was an intrusion, his coming over here. She hadn't invited him; she didn't want him to come. In fact, there was no reason why she had to put up with it, and she wouldn't.

With an air of righteous decision she telephoned Sunny King's residence. Trevor Haines answered the call and she took the opportunity of asking about her car.

'Everything's fine, Mrs Mulholland. No problem. It'll be fitted with a laminated windscreen.'

She frowned over the generosity of the replacement but there was nothing she could do about it now. 'When will I have it back, Mr Haines?'

'Oh, please call me Trevor, Mrs Mulholland. The boys do. And I'm afraid it won't be back for a week or so. Some hold-up with the manufacturers. But not to worry. Sunny doesn't need the Daimler for anything.'

A week! And she would have to do food shopping before the weekend. She needed the use of a car, damn it! 'May I please speak to Mr King?'

'Well, er, he's not available at the moment, Mrs Mulholland. May I take a message?'

Jackie sighed in irritation. What was he doing that he wasn't available? Seducing the cook? She had to stop him from coming over here. Just the thought of seduction was enough to unnerve her. She spoke as firmly as she could.

'Mr King said he was coming over here tonight to discuss our common fence. Please tell him I have no intention of paying for a new fence and if he desperately wants one, he'll have to pay for it himself. The matter is not open for discussion so he can save himself a visit.'

'Could you hold the line a minute, Mrs Mulholland?'

He was gone before she could close the conversation and Jackie's irritation rose as she waited.

'Er, Mrs Mulholland?'

'Yes,' she snapped.

'Sunny said to tell you that he's recognised his Waterloo, even if you haven't, and he has no inclination to save himself. He said he'll talk to you about it when he sees you.'

Her mind buzzed with angry retorts but Trevor Haines was merely the messenger boy and it was obvious that Sunny King was not going to be put off. 'Thank you,' she said politely and slammed the telephone down.

She sat there taking deep breaths to counter the skitterish feeling that was fluttering through her veins. He was coming—she couldn't stop him— and he wouldn't listen to her. She knew he wouldn't. He would just . . . She jumped to her feet and strode into the living-room where the boys were sprawled on the floor watching television.

'Robert! Edmund!'

They turned up expectant faces.

'These are your orders. You are not, I repeat not, under any circumstances whatsoever, to leave me alone with Sunny King. Do you understand?'

'Yes, Mum,' they chorused. They exchanged mystified looks as their mother strode off to her bedroom, then dismissed the matter with expressive shrugs and turned their attention back to *Mysteries Of The Deep*.

Jackie felt hot and bothered and grubby from cleaning the kitchen. She took a quick shower and put on the new sundress she had bought, not because she wanted to look attractive for Sunny King, but because it made her feel better. It was a nice dress with a fresh lime-green and white floral print, and she was entitled to wear a nice dress if she wanted to.

However, the shoestring straps did leave her shoulders bare and the neckline was a trifle low, revealing just the slightest swell of her full breasts. But she was certainly not going to be ruled by what Sunny King might think.

Waterloo indeed! She didn't believe for a minute that she had conquered his heart. Sunny King lived in a fantasy world—his dreadful house was witness to that—and if she was ever fool enough to believe his extravagant talk, that would be her Waterloo. If she succumbed, how long would their relationship last? Two hours at most. And then how would she feel?

Jackie found herself remembering how she had felt this afternoon in the Daimler. Two hours of Sunny King's lovemaking... She hurriedly clamped down on the tempting thought. It was madness. What she had to remember was all his deficiencies in character, and she had ample proofs of those. She couldn't possibly surrender her self-respect to such a man.

On that note of proud determination she swept out to the kitchen, made herself a cup of coffee and joined the boys in the living-room. She tried to concentrate on the television programme but her gaze kept drifting to the clock and her ears were listening for the sound of the Lagonda.

The programme ended at eight-thirty. The boys then chose to watch an old western movie. Time crept on ... nine o'clock ... nine-fifteen ... nine-thirty ... Jackie's nerves were frayed to snapping point. It was just what she should have expected from Sunny King, an ill-mannered, uncivilised notoriety seeker. No consideration. He would keep the whole world waiting without a thought for anyone but himself.

Maybe he had decided to take her at her word

and wasn't calling at all. The thought brought an odd feeling of anti-climax. Almost disappointment. No, it was relief, Jackie told herself decisively. Then the vibrant resonance of a well-tuned engine assailed her ears and her heart leapt into her throat.

The squeal of tyres and the sound of sprayed gravel ricocheting around the garden left no doubt on the matter. Sunny King had arrived. Jackie bit her lips. The man was an ass, an extroverted show-off with the mentality of a child. She stood up, gathered her dignity about her, walked down the hallway, switched on the outside light and opened the front door.

He got out of the car and Jackie was relieved to see that he was fully clothed for once, however eccentric his fashion choice was: loose white trousers that suggested pyjama bottoms and a baggy white shirt with pockets everywhere and only one button done up near his waist. A couple of fine gold chains gleamed on the expanse of tanned chest on show.

He grinned at her, eyes sparkling with devilish anticipation. 'Sorry to be early. I didn't want to disturb the children before you sent them to bed, but in the end I couldn't wait any longer.'

Early! Jackie immediately bristled at the implications of his blithe greeting. It certainly wasn't early for an innocent discussion of fences and she could only think of one reason why he wanted the boys out of the way. He was closing the gap between them rapidly, bounding up the steps to the veranda. Jackie retreated a pace into the hallway.

'The boys don't go to bed early during school holidays. They're waiting up for you.' It gave her enormous satisfaction to slap that information in his face and even more satisfaction to see that it halted him in his tracks.

But only for a moment. He stepped forward, lifted his arms and hung his hands on the lintel above the door, seeming to flaunt his body at her with arrogant confidence in his own attractions. And God help her, she did find him strongly attractive, and he knew it! But it was only physical, Jackie fiercely reminded herself.

'In that case, I think we should go down and inspect the fences. Together. Alone. So you can see at first hand what I mean.' The soft words sang with suggestiveness.

Her pulse pounded into overdrive. There could be no doubt about his intentions now. A roll in the grass would do him if he couldn't have an immediate tumble in bed. 'I'll call the boys,' she said quickly and was already turning when a hand dropped on to her shoulder, making her pause, causing her heart to play leapfrog with itself.

'Don't do that,' he said quietly. The hand slid away, with a finger lightly tracing a shoestring strap to the soft swell of breast. 'I like your dress. It suits you,' he added with a winning smile.

She was not going to be putty in his too-experienced hands. Jackie retreated another pace, out of easy reach. She took a deep, steadying breath and gave it to him straight. 'Mr King, you seem to have the wrong idea about me. I might be a widow but I'm not available to jump into bed with the first man who comes along; and certainly, if I had any inclination along those lines, that man wouldn't be you.'

He laughed at her.

She desperately hung on to her dignity. 'Now, please do be sensible, Mr King.'

His eyes sparkled. 'Be a devil. Let yourself go.'

'Can't you think of anything else?' she demanded in exasperation.

'Not when I'm with you,' he grinned.

'Don't be ridiculous!' she snapped, losing patience with him and doing her best to shut off the wicked thoughts that were popping into her mind.

'From the first moment I saw you ...'

'The answer is no!'

'... I promised myself that you would be my woman.'

'No, no, no!'

His eyebrows slanted appealingly. 'You must realise that at heart I'm the last of the great romantics. That's why I'm so successful. And that's why you appeal to me so much.'

'I've never heard such bombastic nonsense in all my life,' Jackie scorned.

He dropped his other hand from the lintel and Jackie retreated another pace. Words weren't a problem. She was in control as long as they were just trading words, but if he got too close she might be in trouble, no matter what her mind said. He leaned against the door-jamb and slowly, deliberately folded his arms, all the time grinning at her, mocking her fear.

'I think I'll make a movie about our relationship,' he said whimsically.

'We haven't got a relationship,' she answered loftily.

He chuckled and reached out an inviting hand. 'It would be a huge success. Now come down and look at the fences with me. I have a vision . . .'

'You are preposterous!'

'I'm going to knock it all down. Everything.'

She shook her head in confusion. 'Knock what down?'

He made a sweeping gesture. 'The fence is the first to go. Then that ugly brick kiln and the ramshackle sheds . . .'

'No,' Jackie breathed in disbelief.

'Then this house. Knock 'em all down. Bring in the biggest bulldozer you've ever seen. Raze 'em to the ground.'

Her hands planted themselves on her hips in indignation. 'Don't even dare to think such a thing! This is my home and . . .'

'Think what a superb view I'll have when they're all gone.' He refolded his arms and his whole body emanated smugness.

Jackie stamped her foot at him. 'You're crazy! This is crazy talk!'

He blithely ignored the accusation.

She flounced to the opposite side of the hallway, leaned her back on the wall, folded her own arms and glared at him. 'I'd never permit it and you wouldn't get away with it.'

His eyes laughed at her. 'That's what I was told before I made *Eye For An Eye*. Impossible. Can't be done. But I did it. Our children ...'

'You haven't got any children.'

'That's why we have to get started as soon as possible. How old are you, anyway? Must have been a child-bride. Plenty of years for us to ...'

'Will you stop this?' Jackie shrilled, sheer incredulity driving her voice high. 'You don't even know me. And I don't like you. How can you talk about us having children?'

He gave her a look of reproach. 'Take the grand approach to life. Don't think in trivia. You know you want me. We'd make a great couple.'

Jackie took a deep, calming breath. For some unaccountable reason her heart was leaping all over the place. 'Are you actually proposing to me?'

His smile was pure lechery. 'When we touch our minds are in harmony. You have the loveliest breasts I've ever seen. And the grandest hips. What more can a man want? I'll make you mine and never let you go.'

Nothing but sex on his mind! Just as she had thought. A lot of empty words just to get her to go to bed with him. She had to end his little game before he got her confused again.

'Mr King, your imagination has run riot. The answer to all your propositions is no, no, no, and no! You're not knocking my fence down. If you come near my kiln, or my sheds, or my house, with your bulldozer, I'll blast you with both barrels of my shotgun. And anyone who cohabited with you would have to be certifiably insane.'

He looked peeved. 'You don't like me much yet, do you?'

'That is a masterpiece of meiosis.'

'What's that mean?' he demanded suspiciously.

'Understatement,' Jackie replied with succinct satisfaction. 'I find you abhorrent, rude ...'

'Now hold on there! You're a mite rash with your words. I looked troglodyte up in the dictionary, and I'm not at all like a primitive gorilla.'

But Jackie's tongue was in full spate, recklessly intent on hitting back at him for threatening her. 'We don't all see ourselves as others see us,' she quipped.

'You'll come to see my good points.'

'I doubt it.'

He unfolded his arms and straightened up and his eyes held a purposeful gleam. 'I can see we need some other form of communication. Kiss me.' He took a step towards her.

'Robert! Edmund! Come here this instant,' she shrieked.

'We're just here, Mum,' Robert answered promptly, and she turned to see both boys levering themselves up from the floor on either side of the doorway into the living-room. It was only then that she realised that the television was off.

'Have you been listening?' she demanded, absolutely appalled at the thought.

Robert took it upon himself to reply. 'You told us we weren't to leave you alone with Sunny King, Mum, so when you didn't bring him in, and you didn't call us out, we thought we'd better hold a watching brief.'

Oh, God! Hoist on her own petard! They'd heard every word!

Sunny King chuckled. 'Well, well, well! How very interesting to find out that you can't trust yourself alone with me, Mrs Mulholland.'

I'll kill them, Jackie thought wildly. If they don't kill themselves I'll surely do those boys in. She swung back to Sunny King, breathing fire. 'It's you I don't trust. And let me tell you that anyone who trespasses on my property is going to get blasted.'

He sobered, but fixed her with a determined eye. 'The fence goes.'

'Only if you're prepared to replace it at your own expense.'

'Then the kiln.'

'Just you try it and see what you get!'

'Then the house.'

'Over my dead body!'

'And then you. I'm going to take you under my wing and give you all you deserve.'

'Please go before I lose my temper, Mr King.'

'I wish you sweet dreams of love. I'll win, you know.'

'Not bloody likely!'

He laughed and gave her a mocking wave of farewell. 'Goodnight, my love.'

'Goodbye!' she yelled after him, but only his laughter answered her.

She slammed the front door shut, snapped off

the outside light and wheeled on her two sons. Their eyes were alive with fascinated interest and she felt pinned by them, unable to explain or excuse the conversation they had overheard.

Edmund broke the impasse, speaking with a respect he rarely showed. 'Mum, that was the greatest adult conversation we've ever listened to. Much better than the TV.'

Robert offered a more critical viewpoint. 'Why didn't you say yes, Mum? We think it would be terrific to have Sunny King as our father.'

'Bed!' she croaked and swallowed hard to get more authority in to her voice. 'Go to bed. I don't want to discuss what you've heard. I don't want you to talk about it. Just forget Sunny King and go to bed. Right this minute.'

'But . . .' Edmund began, and received a swift kick to the ankle from Robert.

'OK, Mum. Night,' he said tactfully.

'Night, Mum,' Edmund echoed obediently.

'But she kissed him the other night,' Jackie heard him hiss at Robert as they went off to their bedroom.

She sagged back against the front door and ran a trembling hand over her forehead. She had to pull herself together. She never lost her temper. Hardly ever. She was an easy-going person, almost placid. She had calmly dealt with everything life had tossed up to her—until now.

It hadn't been easy. Being married to Geoff had had its problems. He had never been very organised over domestic affairs, and she had kept everything in order when he was off on his expeditions. She was really a very level-headed, capable woman, not given to panic or any excesses in temperament.

So how come Sunny King could make her fall to pieces?

It was ridiculous; it had to stop. She couldn't carry on like this. Not only was he undermining her own sense of security but he was undermining her relationship with her children, making her feel a fool in front of them. He was not to be let near her again, even if she had to stop him with the ultimate weapon. Him and his bulldozer. Just let him try! She'd get him with both barrels of the shotgun all right.

CHAPTER FIVE

Two days later the bulldozer turned up. Jackie immediately went to the gun cupboard, unlocked it, found the cartridges for the shotgun and loaded it. She stalked out to the veranda, all primed to protect hearth and home. If Sunny King's henchmen came anywhere near the kiln or the sheds or the house with their bulldozer, they'd be met with more than verbal resistance. By God they would!

The bulldozer headed straight for the fence. The old posts went down like matchsticks before the might of the machine, and within an hour the fence was gone. The bulldozer dug a large hole and buried the lot. Jackie didn't mind the dangerous strands of rusty barbed wire being safely disposed of under a metre of earth, but the posts could have been used for firewood. The utter wastefulness of it fed her resentment of Sunny King's high-handed actions.

The bulldozer started trundling up the old fence-line. Jackie raced down to the brick kiln and took up guard, but the monstrous machine did not deviate from its route. The driver gave her a cheery wave as he went past. She followed him up to the road and saw the bulldozer reloaded on its float-truck.

'You're not coming back?' she demanded suspiciously.

'Do you want a job done?' the operator asked. 'Save you the cost of floating the 'dozer if I do it now.'

'No, thank you. I just want to know if you're finished here, or if Mr King has other orders for you.'

'Not today he hasn't. Just get rid of the fence.' He gazed down the bare line with satisfaction. 'All neat and tidy for him. Starting on the new one this afternoon, he said.' He nodded at the gun. 'Shooting rabbits?'

'No. Just ready for trespassing llamas,' she retorted grimly.

The operator gave her a wary look that wondered if she'd lost her marbles, said a hasty goodbye, and swung up into the cabin of his truck.

Jackie didn't care what he thought. She was glad to see him and his bulldozer leave and know that they weren't coming back. Not today, anyway. She locked up the shotgun and headed down to the pottery shed, needing some activity to relax her taut nerves.

Usually she found working with clay very soothing but she couldn't get her mind concentrated on it at all. Thoughts of Sunny King kept distracting her, making her more and more irritable, and her work suffered accordingly. When she went up to the house to have some lunch, the boys were already in the kitchen cutting sandwiches, their clothes absolutely filthy and their hands only given a token washing.

'If I've told you once, I've told you a thousand times, do not touch food with dirty hands,' she ordered, doing her best to hold on to her frayed temper. 'What in the world have you been doing to get yourselves in such a mess?'

'Playing in the dirt the bulldozer dug up. It's great for making roads and things,' Robert explained with unabashed enthusiasm.

'We're making a Grand Prix race-track,' Edmund chimed in. 'And we did wash our hands, Mum.'

They grabbed their sandwiches and zoomed out of the door before she could voice any protests or point out any more deficiencies in hygiene. With a sigh of exasperation, Jackie wiped up the dusty footprints on the kitchen floor and harboured thoughts of sending the dirty laundry over to Sunny King. Except he would have someone else do it.

Then the truckload of new fence-posts arrived, along with a pole-driving machine that fired them into the ground with the force and noise of a cannon. Jackie brooded through the barrage of sound, having abandoned all hope of doing any creative work. Another truck arrived and a team of fencing contractors got to work, bolting railings to the posts.

No ordinary wire fence for Sunny King, Jackie thought sourly, but, as she watched it go up, she had to admit it was a vast improvement on the old one. Undoubtedly he would have it painted white

like the rest of the fences on his property. The cost
of maintenance wouldn't worry him. All he cared
about was his view.

She walked outside and took a long, hard look at
what Sunny King saw of her place. It was an old
house and the paint was peeling. It had seemed so
charming when she and Geoff had bought it ten
years ago. Boys should be brought up in the
country, he had said, and of course she had agreed
with him. Still agreed. But old places needed
looking after and she didn't have the money to do
it.

When Geoff had died he had left her the
unencumbered property and a small insurance
policy which her investment adviser had managed
to good effect, but the income was only enough for
subsistence living. Her pottery paid for the running
of the car and the extra things the boys required
from time to time, but it was going to take a lot of
pottery to get the house re-painted.

And the sheds did look ramshackle. The garage
walls had a slight lean and the doors didn't meet
properly. The roofing was rusty and leaked in
places. As for the kiln, she supposed it did look
ugly, with its blackened bricks. Nevertheless, it still
worked, and that was the main thing.

The thought didn't do much to lift Jackie's
spirits. Depression rolled over her as she considered
the future. Robert was starting high school this
year and Edmund wasn't far behind. Life was not
going to be so simple for ever. She had to do

something about getting them on to a better financial footing.

Whether they sensed her inner distress or not Jackie did not know, but the boys were particularly helpful and considerate that night, doing the washing up after tea and going to bed early without being told. It did surprise her when they begged off going shopping in the Daimler the next morning, but she was inwardly relieved that she didn't have to worry about their fooling around in Sunny King's car. She assumed that the Grand Prix race-track was still under construction.

Jackie was too nervous about driving the Daimler to go all the way to the supermarket in Windsor. She could buy most of what she needed at Wiseman's Ferry and she would make do until her own car was returned, even if the food did cost a bit more. It was a mistake she very soon regretted. Having lived in the area for over ten years, all the local people knew her and her possession of a Daimler raised eyebrows.

'Got a new car, Mrs Mulholland,' the ferry master observed. 'Very nice. Very nice indeed,' he added, his eyes full of dollar question marks.

'No, it's not mine,' she said hurriedly. 'I've just got the loan of it while mine's being repaired.'

'Very obliging garage!' he commented drily.

'Not the garage. My, er, neighbour lent it to me.'

'Very obliging neighbour.' His eyes sharpened with speculation. 'Sunny King bought next to you, didn't he?'

'Yes, that's right,' she muttered, a tide of

warmth creeping up her neck.

'A-hah. Become good friends, have you?'

'Just neighbours,' Jackie grated.

And that was only the beginning. It was the same everywhere she went. Sunny King's generosity fired everyone's imagination. It didn't matter how she tried to explain it, she could see that her reputation was ruined; no one was going to believe that there wasn't something going on between her and Sunny King. She was on the verge of tears all the way home.

The boys didn't answer her call so she had to carry the parcels in by herself, which added to her feeling that the whole world was against her. They were late coming up from the paddock for lunch, too, and when she walked down to the back yard to yell out to them, they were nowhere to be seen. Gone for a dip in the river, Jackie decided, and didn't worry about them. They could both swim like fish and no doubt they would appear when they were hungry enough.

But they didn't appear, and by three o'clock Jackie felt annoyed enough to walk down to the river. There was no sign of them and no answer to her calls. Anger built with every step back to the house. They were supposed to leave a note if they were going to a friend's house. Hadn't she drummed that into them? She'd teach them a lesson all right. They could come on home right now, no matter what marvellous game they were playing.

However, several telephone calls elicited the fact

that none of their friends had seen either Robert or Edmund all day. Jackie's anger gathered an edge of anxiety. Where the devil were they and what were they doing? Could they have got themselves into trouble? They were not stupid, she told herself; adventurous but not stupid. If one was hurt the other would go for help. No need to panic.

But her anxiety mounted as hour after hour crawled by. She took to pacing the veranda on the lookout for them. Teatime came and went. Anxiety built into fear. What would she do if they hadn't come home by dark? Where could they be?

The sun was setting when she finally spotted them, running across the paddock beyond the new fence. The sick relief she felt churned into monumental anger. They were on Sunny King's property, coming from the direction of Sunny King's house. That irresponsible, feckless playboy was at the bottom of this escapade.

Robert waited at the fence for Edmund who was lagging badly, obviously exhausted from whatever they had been doing. They had angled their run so that their approach would be from the direction of the river and Jackie went to greet them at the back door. Robert was talking fast and furiously to Edmund, who was nodding wearily. They did not see their mother until she spoke.

'And just where have you been?' she demanded in an ominous tone.

'Sorry, Mum. We didn't realise how late it was getting,' Robert babbled at high speed.

'You haven't answered my question, Robert.'

'We went bird-watching.'

Which was an out and out lie! She could see evasion written all over their faces.

'Oh, and what birds did you see, Edmund?' she asked silkily.

'Er . . . kookaburras, magpies, cockatoos, rosellas and . . . er . . . lots more.'

'Well, that's very interesting. I didn't think Sunny King would be interested in birds of the feathered kind.'

'He didn't go with us, Mum,' Edmund denied stoutly.

'Then who did go with you, Edmund?'

He suddenly realised he had fallen into a trap and looked at Robert for guidance.

Robert reluctantly shouldered the responsibility. 'It was Trevor Haines, Mum.'

Trevor Haines . . . Jackie's mind whirred and clicked. She turned and fired straight at Edmund. 'Did you go abseiling?'

The shock on his face gave the game away. Jackie was so furious, she couldn't trust herself to speak. She pointed inside and the boys quickly ducked under her arm and raced for the bathroom. Jackie went into the kitchen to prepare tea for them. There was murder in her heart.

How dared Sunny King and Trevor Haines involve her children in something as spectacularly dangerous as going up and down cliffs on ropes? They should be strung up on ropes themselves. Of course the boys had to be punished for their disobedience, but the main blame could be laid fairly and squarely on the doorstep of 'King's Folly'. And the leader in that folly was surely Sunny King.

So this was his next move, seducing her sons away from her authority! Getting them on his side so she couldn't look to them for any support against him. How underhand could he get, just to win his own way?

When the boys finally presented themselves, all scrubbed up and in their pyjamas, they looked so tired, Jackie didn't have the heart to take them to task tonight. Besides, she was immensely relieved to have them home safe and sound. Lectures and punishment could wait until tomorrow. And she would have a few choice words to say to Trevor Haines and Sunny King tomorrow, too.

The boys slept late the next morning and Jackie had only just finished laying down the law to them when the now-familiar sound effects of Sunny King's driving heralded his arrival in the front yard. The blast of the Lagonda's horn to reinforce the announcement did nothing to lighten Jackie's mood. She went straight to the gun cupboard and armed herself with the shotgun. Sunny King was just alighting from his car when she stepped out on the the veranda.

'Good morning!' he called cheerfully as he caught sight of her. 'Lovely morning, isn't it?'

Jackie moved to the top of the front steps and pointed the gun at him. 'Stay right where you are, Mr Sunny King. Don't move another step!'

He looked startled for a moment then mockingly

raised his hands. 'What kind of reception is this? Just when we've got on to first name terms too. I've been wanting to hear my name on your lips ever . . .'

'Just what did you think you were doing with my children yesterday?' she cut in savagely.

'I did nothing. Trevor took them abseiling. He told me they really enjoyed themselves. Now please put the gun down and let me come on to the veranda. It's hot out here in the sun.'

'You can bake in hell for all I care. You knew about this abseiling, didn't you? You let them go. You didn't care if they fell and broke their necks,' she accused with venom.

'What's all the fuss about? They got home safely, didn't they?'

'No thanks to you. You don't care about anyone but yourself.'

'Now that's not true . . .'

But Jackie wasn't listening. She was in full spate. 'I haven't known a moment's peace since you started building that damned whorehouse over there. Now you just get back in your car and get out of my life. And you can send your equally irresponsible secretary over here to pick up your other damned car, too. I don't want it.'

His hands lowered into a gesture of appeal. 'Please put the gun down and let's talk about . . .'

'I don't want to talk to you.'

'I have a proposition . . .'

'The answer's no.'

'You haven't heard it yet.'

'It doesn't matter.'

His hands dropped to his hips and he shook his head at her in reproof. 'I won't take no for an answer. You've tried and convicted me in a kangaroo court and now I'm going to open your mind.'

He stepped forward. Jackie swung the gun up to her shoulder and cocked it. 'Take one more step and I'll shoot.'

He stopped and heaved a sigh. 'OK, I don't mind dying in the cause of love. Where are you going to shoot me?'

'In the stomach.'

He considered her with a critical eye. 'That would be more than painful.'

'Dead right!'

'Can't we reach a compromise?'

'No.'

He huffed in exasperation, seemed about to swing away, then had the gall to grin at her. 'I'm coming to get you.'

Her heart did something curious and there was a rush of blood to her head. 'Don't try it,' she screeched.

He stepped forward. The blast of the gun spun Jackie around. The noise stunned her into immobility.

'God almighty! You fired it!'

The shocked utterances from Sunny King sped Jackie's recovery. 'That was a warning shot,' she declared shakily. 'Be grateful I didn't hit you.'

'Grateful!' he roared at her. 'I felt the bloody

pellets whizzing past my head, you crazy woman!'

He started towards her, vengeful purpose written all over him.

'I'll shoot again,' she screamed. 'I've still got one barrel left.'

Edmund came pelting out on to the veranda, yelling at the top of his voice. 'Robert! Come and look at this! Mum's trying to kill Sunny King.'

That did it. The split second of lapse in concentration as she looked at Edmund allowed Sunny King to get to her. The shotgun was torn from her hands and hurled away. Then he was lifting her up, shaking her, his face working with fury as he spouted forth a stream of righteous anger.

'Call me irresponsible! How mad can you get, shooting to maim and kill? I'm going to wallop your bottom until it puts some sense in your head. I'm going to wallop it until your brain thinks straight. I'm going to give you something you'll remember me by for the rest of your life. And thank me for it. I'm going to . . .'

'No, no, no!' Jackie wailed, arms flailing, legs kicking—but to no effect.

He was hoisting her into a position to carry out his threat, words still frothing from his mouth. Jackie tried to catch at the veranda post in a vain attempt to keep herself upright. She looked desperately around for some other form of help as he started to lower himself into a sitting position on the front step. What she saw froze the blood in her veins.

'Edmund! she screamed. 'Put that gun down!'

Sunny King sat down with thump, Jackie strewn across his lap. The flow of words had ceased with her frightened shriek. He stared at Edmund who had picked up the shotgun and was pointing it at them.

'God Almighty!' Sunny King breathed in horror. 'The whole family's mad.' He raised his voice to a bull-like roar. 'Point the bloody thing at me, you stupid boy, not at your mother.' Then suddenly he was rolling, taking Jackie with him, shielding her with his body. 'Bring that gun to me,' he commanded.

'You're going to hurt my mother,' Edmund retorted in stubborn defiance.

'I'm not hurting your mother. I'm protecting her from her idiot son. Bring that gun over here and give it to me.'

Half-smothered as she was, Jackie struggled for breath. 'Do as he says, Edmund,' she gasped. 'If I'd wanted him shot I'd have done it myself.'

Edmund remained steadfast. 'Dirk Vescum wouldn't give up,' he declared.

Sunny King muttered a vicious curse. 'Dirk Vescum hates violence!' he roared. 'He certainly wouldn't do anything that could endanger innocent people's lives. Now hand over that goddamned gun, and I'll get off your mother. You're the one who's hurting her.'

'Better do as he says, Edmund,' Robert put in.

The aim of the gun wavered away as Edmund glanced up at his brother. 'He's pretty big and he's really angry,' Edmund argued.

'There's three of us against him,' Robert pointed out. 'Give it over.'

The barrel dragged on to the ground as Edmund reluctantly did Robert's bidding. Sunny King snatched it from him, sprang to his feet, strode out to the front yard and fired it into the air, emptying it of ammunition.

The anguish that Sunny King had caused her over over the last few days suddenly combined with the fear of the last few minutes, and Jackie gave vent to it all as she climbed to her feet. 'See what you do with your rotten Dirk Vescum movies!' she shrieked.

'What I do!' he bellowed in fierce indignation. 'My God! Just wait till I get my hands on you.'

Jackie shrank back as he wheeled on her in a towering rage. Robert leapt the veranda railing and put himself between them. He was instantly joined by Edmund, both of them with their fists raised ready to fight. It brought Sunny King up short.

'We're not going to let you hurt our mother,' Robert stated belligerently.

Sunny King shook his head in disbelief. 'They're all mad. Not a grain of sense anywhere.' He raised his gaze to Jackie, blue eyes blazing. 'And I came over here to do you a favour!' he roared.

'I don't want your two-faced favours,' she screamed back at him. 'The best favour you can do for me is to go away and stay away.'

His mouth clamped into a grim line as he briefly studied her intransigent attitude. 'Fine!' he spat out. 'That's fine by me. And I'm taking this gun with me. I'm not going to be shot in the back by a fool of a woman who doesn't know what's good for her.'

He marched over to the Lagonda, tossed the gun into the back seat, climbed in, slammed the door, switched on the engine and, with an almighty burst of acceleration, wheeled the car around and screamed out on to the road.

'He's gone, Mum,' Robert stated unnecessarily.

'Yeah. We saved you, Mum,' Edmund said with manly satisfaction.

Jackie slumped down on the steps and burst into tears.

CHAPTER SIX

How could she have done such a dreadful thing? Geoff had told her, so many times, never, never, never to point a gun at anybody. Not for any reason. She hadn't meant to shoot. Not really. She had only meant to frighten him off. But giving such a terrible example to her sons! If Edmund had pulled the trigger ... The thought of the consequences made her shudder.

And Sunny King shielding her with his own body. Shielding her when she was the one at fault. So what thanks did she give him? Instead of backing him up when he had defused the dangerous situation she had screamed more abuse at him. He had every right to be angry. Every right. She was a total fool.

'Don't cry, Mum,' Robert pleaded. 'It's all right now.'

'It's not all right,' she sobbed. 'Everything's wrong. I haven't got the money to fix the place up, and you boys just go drifting off whenever you feel like it, and not telling me; and you could have got yourselves killed, and Edmund could have killed us this morning ...' More tears gushed from her eyes and she covered her face with her hands. Her whole body shook with sobs of despair.

Edmund sat down beside her and patted her

back. 'I wouldn't have shot you, Mum,' he assured her.

'And we wouldn't have gone abseiling without someone who knew all about it,' Robert explained. 'Trevor's had lots of experience.'

'He had no right to take you,' Jackie wailed. 'I told you no. Sunny King had no right to take it upon himself to . . . to override my authority.'

'Well, er, you can't really blame him, Mum. We figured it was safe to go with Trevor so we sort of . . . er gave Sunny the impression that you'd OK'd it.'

'Yeah, and he even tried to check with you but we made sure you'd gone shopping first,' Edmund supplied in the hope of making her feel better.

'We thought we'd get home earlier so you wouldn't notice, but we got stuck on a ledge for a while and . . .'

'How could you?' Jackie burst out, absolutely beside herself. 'How could you tell such terrible lies? And I blamed Sunny King for letting you go.'

'They weren't real lies, Mum,' Edmund insisted.

'We just skirted around the whole truth. I mean we were bird-watching, too,' Robert argued with all the guile of a defence counsel. 'Please don't cry, Mum. We promise we'll do all the fixing up around the house for you. Just tell us what you want done.'

'Yeah. We'll make it up to you, Mum,' Edmund added soulfully. 'We'll be real good.'

Which left Jackie feeling even more defeated. The boys were getting beyond her control. Maybe they'd always been beyond her control. They just let her think she was in charge occasionally.

Robert took her hand. 'Come on in, Mum. Lie down for a while. I'll bring you a cup of coffee. You'll feel better soon.'

But Jackie didn't although the tears eventually dried up. She had wronged Sunny King, and Trevor Haines. But most especially Sunny King. Her only real grievance against him was the broken windscreen and he had more than redressed that wrong. She couldn't really take offence at the fact that he had considered her desirable, particularly since she hadn't exactly fought him off when he'd been kissing her. He wasn't to blame for what other people thought, either. And the new fence added value to her property.

So he was an arrogant show-off who thought the whole world was his personal oyster. That was no reason for her to shoot a gun at him. She was deeply ashamed of her unwarranted behaviour, even more ashamed as she kept remembering how he had protected her with his own body. He could have used her as a hostage for his own safety, but instead he had safeguarded her as best he could against any possibility of harm.

She owed him an apology, an abject apology; there was no getting away from that. The thought tormented her all day. The boys were model sons, Robert mowing all the grass, Edmund weeding the garden and making neat piles of all the rubbish lying around. After tea the boys settled down to a game of Monopoly, and Jackie could not put off her conscience any longer.

'I have to go and talk to Mr King,' she announced. 'I don't know how long I'll be. You're to go to bed at nine o'clock. And I mean nine o'clock.'

'Yes, Mum. Double promise,' Robert replied for both of them.

'We're tired from all that work anyway,' Edmund muttered, shaking the dice out on to the Monopoly board.

And so much for my authority, Jackie thought despondently. She drove the Daimler up the road to Sunny King's house. She couldn't keep his car any longer, not after what she had done. Somehow she and the boys would survive on what supplies she had in the house until her own car was returned.

Trevor Haines answered the doorbell and greeted her cheerily, obviously still ignorant of the morning's disastrous fiasco. But that didn't alleviate Jackie's inner misery. She had to confess to her own sons' perfidy.

'Mr Haines . . .'

'Oh, please, call me Trevor. Sorry about being a bit late home with the boys yesterday, Mrs Mulholland. Hope you weren't worried.'

'Well, yes, I was. I'm afraid they misled you, Trevor. I had expressly forbidden them to go abseiling. Please don't think I blame you, as I'm aware of how . . . how devious they can be.'

He went beetroot-red. 'I say, I'm most terribly sorry. Sunny did try to phone you, but . . .'

'I know,' Jackie sighed. 'Robert and Edmund do tend to plan things very well. However, I'd appreciate it if you didn't take their word for anything from now on. Please check with me personally.'

'I most certainly will, Mrs Mulholland.'

Jackie took a deep breath. 'And now I'd like to speak to Mr King, if he's home.'

Trevor visibly dithered. 'Oh . . . er . . . I promise you it won't happen again, Mrs Mulholland.'

He really was very young. 'It has nothing to do with yesterday, Trevor,' she assured him. 'It's about a personal matter between Mr King and myself.'

'Aah!' He brightened. 'Please come in. I'm sure Sunny will be happy to see you.'

Jackie was not at all sure that Sunny King wouldn't order her out of his house, but she was grateful for Trevor Haines's innocent welcome. Grateful, also, that Sunny King hadn't seen fit to regale his secretary with details of this morning's madness.

'Sunny's watching an old movie down in the theatre,' Trevor informed her. 'I'll take you down.'

'Thank you,' Jackie murmured, and followed him with increasing nervousness.

The theatre was in darkness, apart from the big screen. Jackie took one look at the black and white picture of Ingrid Bergman and Humphrey Bogart and recognised the film as *Casablanca*. Which rather surprised her.

'Sunny . . .' Trevor hissed.

The dark silhouette of Sunny King, slumped in one of the sofas on the far side of the room, made no move.

'Mrs Mulholland is here to see you,' Trevor announced confidently.

For a couple of nerve-racking moments Jackie thought Sunny King was going to ignore both of them. Then he leaned forward. The picture on the screen flicked off and an overhead light flicked on. He slowly rose to his feet, his face quite expressionless as he turned towards them.

'Thank you, Trevor,' he said coldly.

It was a dismissal, plain and simple, and Trevor needed no second hint. He closed the door quietly behind him, leaving Jackie to face Sunny King alone—which was what she wanted; but she felt hopelessly tongue-tied now that the moment of reckoning had come.

'Would you care for a glass of muscat?' Sunny King asked, waving to the bottle that stood on the low table in front of him.

'No. No, thank you,' she choked out.

He shrugged and sat down again, apparently having decided that any further gesture of hospitality would be wasted on her. He stared at the blank screen, completely ignoring her presence. His moody expression held a strong resemblance to that of her boys when they were sulking. Had she wounded his pride so deeply?

'*Casablanca* is one of the great movies,' she remarked, in an attempt to break the ice.

'Yes. It's about honour, and loyalty, and love,

and chivalry, and fair play.' He gave a feeling emphasis to every point.

A flush of shame burnt into Jackie's cheeks but he spoke on without giving her a chance to make her apology.

'Sentiments that aren't very fashionable these days, and yet they mean a great deal to me. But you don't see that, do you? To you I'm a rude and abhorrent troglodyte. A thing you shoot at.'

Oh, God! What had she done? Jackie had not known what to expect from him but somehow she had never considered that the irresponsible Sunny King had feelings that could be deeply hurt. Never had she felt so mean. So small. And she deserved every bit of his accusation.

He took a sip from his glass, then held it up to her in a mock toast. 'Perhaps you'll enlighten me as to why you've come to this whorehouse, Mrs Mulholland.'

Jackie swallowed hard to moisten her throat and forced the words out. 'I came to apologise, for myself and my sons.'

His eyes were hard, unforgiving, and he spoke with icy deliberation. 'Don't do that for your sons, Mrs Mulholland. As misguided as they were in their actions, I would have done precisely what they did in defence of my own mother. They love you deeply.'

His generosity threw her into confusion again. 'Then . . . then I'm most terribly sorry for what I said and did. I . . . I misunderstood things. But I know that's no excuse, and I'm not trying to excuse myself. I was wrong and stupid and ... and I'm sorry.'

He took another mouthful of wine and his mouth curled sardonically over the glass. 'You've handed out quite a few insults, and I would like to know one thing, before I decide whether your apology is worth accepting or not.'

'And what's that?' Jackie asked, feeling more mortified than ever.

'Have you seen either one of the Dirk Vescum movies?'

The question surprised her until a few moments' reflection brought the realisation that he was fiercely proud of those movies and she had scorned and belittled them. 'No, I haven't,' she confessed miserably.

'So you condemn, unseen and unheard.'

The statement hung flatly in the air. It made Jackie feel that she had been a little unfair. She tried to explain. 'They do have a reputation for violence, and I abhor ...' She stopped, too conscious of her own actions to defend herself.

Sunny King's smile was savagely ironic. 'There comes a time where violence can only be answered by violence, to prevent something worse happening,' he stated with pointed emphasis. 'However, that's something you have to make up your own mind about. If your apology is sincere, you'll give me a fair hearing.

'I ... I don't understand.'

'I'll show you *Eye For An Eye* from start to finish.' He waved a careless invitation. 'Take a seat,

Mrs Mulholland. Any one will do. As far away from me as you like.' He paused, eyeing her cynically. 'Or you can stuff your apology into your closed mind and walk out. Please yourself.'

She owed him that, Jackie acknowledged. Even if she hated the film and all it represented, sitting through it was a punishment she deserved. She walked stiffly to the closest armchair and sat down.

He stared at her for a few long minutes, finished his drink, walked to the back of the room and opened a cupboard which contained many rows of video recordings. He placed one in a machine, walked back to the table, pressed a control which switched off the overhead light, and lounged back on the sofa he had occupied when she entered the room.

The movie began. Jackie half-knew its story, having been force-fed the more lurid details by Robert and Edmund. It was a simple and hackneyed theme, set in an imaginary place at an imaginary time. Dirk Vescum, the hero, refused to fight invading aliens until his wife and family were brutally killed by them. Dirk lost an eye before he himself escaped. From then on he set out on a vendetta of hatred and revenge until he met the beautiful Alena, daughter of a renegade earthling, who gave him a more balanced purpose for living. Together they halted the alien challenge.

The story was trite, just as Jackie had anticipated. What she hadn't anticipated was the emotional manner in which Sunny King had developed it. There were moments in the love-death scenes which wrung her heart and almost moved her to tears. It wasn't overplayed. It was even understated, but the simplicity of every scene carried its emotional impact with tremendous force.

The action scenes were hectic, riveting with tension and explosive with one shock after another. The violence was certainly there, but it was always implied, never done in gruesome detail. The scenes were choreographed for action-shock and absolutely gripping, despite the lack of costly special effects. The shoestring budget had not cramped the style, and Jackie marvelled at the ingenuity of the man who had got so much out of such limited means.

The development of the relationship between Dirk Vescum and Alena grew from initial antagonism to respect, and then to a reliance on each other's strengths, and not until the closing scene when the aliens had been stopped was there a look of understanding that suggested love might be possible between them.

No sex. Not even a kiss. Alena made a dry comment on the battle and Dirk Vescum looked at her and a smile slowly grew on his face, the first smile since his family had been killed. After a slight hesitation Alena smiled back, and that was the end, leaving the audience on a high note of emotional satisfaction.

Jackie was still caught up in it when the screen went blank and the overhead light glared down. Rather reluctantly she turned her head towards Sunny King. Hard blue eyes bored into her. One eyebrow rose in mocking enquiry.

'Crummy?'

'No, it wasn't crummy.' She searched her mind for an honest comment on what she had seen.

'Rotten?' he tossed at her.

'No.'

'Nothing but abhorrent violence?' he bored on.

Jackie suddenly realised that she had hurt more than his pride with her scathing criticism of his work. She had struck at the heart of the man, for only a man with a very feeling heart and great sensitivity could have made such a film.

'I'm sorry,' she said, her all-too-clever vocabulary completely failing her as she contemplated her dismal failure to give Sunny King his just due. 'It's a grand movie,' she admitted with new-born humility, and she wished with all her heart that he would smile at her as Dirk Vescum had smiled at Alena.

He didn't smile. Not one muscle in his face moved as he continued to stare at her, eyes as hard as diamonds. And she hated it. She wanted the twinkle back, the teasing laughter, anything but that total lack of reaction to her.

'I can now see why it has so much appeal, for such a broad spectrum of audience,' she offered in the hope that it would awaken a spark of interest.

Nothing.

She tried again. 'You chose a great cast. I can't imagine anyone playing the roles better.'

Still nothing.

Almost in desperation, Jackie cast around for

more words of praise, eventually hitting on Sunny King's contribution. 'There wasn't a dull moment. The direction was ... was brilliant.'

Not even that accolade cracked his stony façade.

Jackie felt as if she was being put through a wringer. Finally, limply, she said, 'It surprised me. I liked it. Very much.'

And that produced a response. 'Thank you.' He stood up, still with no softening of expression. 'I'm glad you didn't find it too much of an imposition on your time. If you're ready to go now, I'll see you safely home.'

His icy politeness chilled her to the bone. 'I ... I really am sorry,' she pressed anxiously as she rose to her feet.

'I now accept your apology, Mrs Mulholland.'

He held the door open for her and she really had no other option than to go. Sunny King was finished with her. His whole manner spelled that out with bitter clarity. And it hurt. The way he kept himself frigidly separated from her as they walked up the staircase hurt, too. Jackie told herself that she should have been relieved that any association with Sunny King was over, but she only felt miserable.

When they reached the front doors she couldn't bear it any longer. 'Please don't come any further with me, Mr King.' She held out the keys to the Daimler. 'Thank you for the use of your car. It's just outside near the garage. I won't be needing it any more. And it's only a short walk home. I'll be quite all right.'

He took the keys. 'I'll drive you home. It's dark, and I wish to be sure you get home safely.'

The cold statement brooked no argument. He accompanied her outside and held the passenger door of the Daimler open for her. Jackie slid into it, feeling smaller than ever. Sunny King's studied courtesy was like a slap in the face.

He drove her home at a sedate pace, with none of the squealing of tyres or burning of rubber that she associated with his driving. He slid the car to a quiet halt in her front yard and climbed out, apparently intent on seeing her to her door. For one crazy moment of hope Jackie thought he might suddenly change back into the Sunny King of old and take her in his arms, but he halted at the front steps and made no move to touch her. Jackie hesitated, torn by a dreadful feeling of having burnt bridges she might have liked to cross.

She sought for something to say, to keep him with her a little while longer, to throw some line across the chasm she had dug with her own blind stubbornness.

'Why . . . why did you come here this morning?' she asked, grasping at the one straw that came to mind.

'I wanted to give you something. It doesn't matter any more,' he replied, throwing back the same words she had used this morning. 'Goodnight, Mrs Mulholland.'

She didn't have a leg to stand on. 'Goodnight, Mr King, and thank you for bringing me home,' she said, driven to match his politeness.

He nodded and turned away, striding off towards her gateway without even a glance at the Daimler.

'The car!' she called after him, too agitated by his leaving it not to make some protest.

He half-turned. 'I left the keys in it. Trevor will pick it up when he returns your car. You never know when you might need ready transport and I will not have you deprived of it because of a fault of mine. And before you stand on your pride, Mrs Mulholland, think of your children.'

Having delivered the one unanswerable argument, he turned his back on her and kept walking.

Jackie bit her lips and watched him, her heart sinking with every step he took away from her. She knew he wouldn't come back. Not ever again. And a terrible sense of loss closed in on her.

CHAPTER SEVEN

TREVOR HAINES returned Jackie's car to her the following Thursday. It gleamed like new. The bodywork had been polished and the inside of the car postively sparkled. Jackie felt intensely embarrassed as she accepted the keys from Trevor. The Daimler was sitting in the shed, gathering dust, and she hadn't thought to clean it.

'You didn't have to . . .' She faltered, conscious of sounding ungracious. 'I mean, it looks marvellous, but it wasn't necessary to . . .'

'Oh, the polish job,' Trevor chimed in brightly. 'Nothing to it. Sunny's orders, Mrs Mulholland. There were also a few rust spots that had to be cut out and you'll find the brakes more responsive than they were. You don't have to put your foot right to the floor any more. The brake lining was almost worn through, you know. Very dangerous. And most of the radiator hoses were perishing, so they've been replaced. Sunny had the engine tuned as well, and it's running like a charm.'

Jackie's mind was reeling over the cost of the repairs. She didn't have hundreds of dollars on hand. She had known the brakes needed checking when she put the car in for its next service, but she hadn't realised there was anything else in need of repair.

'I . . . I can't pay. Not until my next cheque

comes,' she said distractedly.

'No need to worry, Mrs Mulholland. It's all been paid for. Sunny said it was too dangerous for you and the kids and the general public, to have you driving around in a car like that. It worried him. I know it did.'

'But it was only supposed to be the windscreen,' she said helplessly. 'I can't accept all this from him.'

'Well, you take that up with Sunny, Mrs Mulholland. I just follow orders.'

She didn't know what to do. She couldn't imagine that Sunny King would take kindly to any argument from her over the matter. Or over any matter, when she came to think about it. On the other hand, she could go and thank him. In fact that was the least she could do in return for his thoughtful generosity.

Jackie had done a good deal of soul-searching over the last few days. The truth was, she had quite enjoyed the few confrontations with Sunny King. He had made her feel more intensely alive than she had felt for years. His high-handed manner had sharpened her wits and the way he had pursued her had been exciting, even though she had denied it to herself at the time. She wanted ... Well, at least she wanted to be on friendly talking terms with him.

'Is Mr King at home?' she asked Trevor as she led him to the Daimler.

'No, he's gone. He suddenly decided to bring his schedule forward a bit. Shooting starts on the new movie next month. Lots of things to check before then. It's going to be the best of the lot, Sunny

STRIKE AT THE HEART

reckons,' Trevor informed her cheerfully.

Jackie's heart sank. 'When will he be back?' she asked, doing her best to project only casual interest.

Trevor shrugged. 'Probably four months or so. Depends on how things go. Bad weather can put you behind. Sunny doesn't do much studio stuff; most of it's on location and he lives with it night and day.'

So that was that, Jackie thought dispiritedly. She could forget Sunny King for four months at least. If she could.

'But there'll be Tom and Betty Willis looking after the place, so you don't have to worry about its being deserted,' Trevor added as he opened the door of the Daimler.

'Who are they?' Jackie asked curiously.

'Housekeeper and handyman. The couple Sunny hired to keep things running. They've got their own apartment at the back of the house.' He settled himself behind the wheel and turned on the ignition. 'I'll be joining Sunny tomorrow. Will you tell the boys goodbye for me?'

'Of course. Thanks, Trevor. And please thank Mr King for me and tell him . . . tell him I hope the movie goes well.' It was a small enough return for his generosity, but it was all she could think of.

'Sure thing, Mrs Mulholland. Bye now.'

She waved him off, then garaged her own car, over-conscious of looking after it now that it was in tip-top condition. It even smelled new. She lingered in the driver's seat, wondering why Sunny King had done all this for her. Trevor had said it was to make sure she would be safe on the road.

Which suggested that Sunny King really cared about her.

She had dismissed his extravagant speech about making her his woman and having children together. She had put that down to his desire to have sex with her. But maybe she was wrong. On Sunday night, when she had offered her apology, Sunny King had acted like a man who had been wounded very deeply. Was it simply ego, or did her opinion of him really matter?

Well, she had effectively killed any softness he had felt for her, Jackie thought with a heavy sigh. He had even put his schedule forward to get out of her way. Though that was probably reading too much into the situation. Maybe when he came back in four months' time ... Well, she would handle things differently, if he gave her the chance.

The summer holidays came to an end and the boys went back to school. Jackie secretly breathed a sigh of relief. School hours prevented them from getting up to too much mischief, although she had to admit they had been very good since the abseiling incident.

Jackie worked long hours at her pottery, intent on building up enough funds to have the house painted. On one of her selling trips to Parramatta she noticed that *Live By The Sword* was still playing at the Village Cinema, and, feeling curiously like a traitor to her own beliefs, she took time off to go and see it. As she sat in the theatre waiting for the main feature to start, she could not quell a lively sense of anticipation and for the first time really understood why the boys had argued so hard about being allowed to see the film.

It opened with the re-establishment of the relationship between Dirk Vescum and Alena, each being commander of a resistance force against the aliens. Without anything being said, it was apparent that Alena was in love with Dirk but he was keeping his distance, wary of committing himself to a deep emotional involvement.

On one of their patrols they rescued a band of half-wild children who were being rounded up by the aliens for experimental purposes. As Dirk led the children to safety, Alena and her two main lieutenants were ambushed. Alena was taken prisoner and her men killed. The main body of the story was the mission to rescue Alena and destroy the aliens' operations. Quite predictably Alena was about to be tortured when Dirk arrived on the scene and beheaded the alien scientists.

However predictable it was, the scene was electric and Jackie was on the edge of her seat, gnawing her knuckles until it was over. Even when Dirk had released Alena there was still no mushiness, as the boys would have put it, only a few moments of great tenderness which spoke volumes, and gave relief to the audience before the wild kids, who had accompanied Dirk, gave the warning that alien troops were arriving.

The battle was incomparable and, when Dirk and Alena finally won, the whole alien centre went up in a massive conflagration. The film ended with Dirk Vescum hugging Alena to him, understanding pulsing between them. However trite it was, Jackie had no doubt that everyone in the audience thought it was a marvellous ending.

In justice to Sunny King, Jackie felt she had to own up to the boys that she had gone to see the movie, and enjoyed seeing it. As she listened to their views over the dinner-table that night, she realised that it wasn't the violence that had enthralled them. Behind the appeal of exciting action was the strong sense of rightness, of good against evil, of feeling for others, of loyalty and bravery and honour and love: the principles and sentiments that Sunny King had told her he held dear.

An egocentric show-off he might be, and his early films were poor, but Jackie certainly couldn't write off the worth of what he was doing now. These last two films, where he had kept personal control on the product, were in another class entirely. They were good entertainment and carried a high level of morality and humanity which won her admiration and approval. There were obviously many dimensions to Sunny King that she had failed to appreciate.

'Well, now you'll come with us to the next Dirk Vescum movie,' Edmund said with happy enthusiasm.

'How do you know there will be a next one?' Jackie asked.

'Trevor told us, but he wouldn't tell us the story,' Robert put in a little plaintively.

'That's why they've gone away,' Edmund explained as if Jackie was singularly thick-headed. 'They're making the next Dirk Vescum movie.'

Over the next few weeks Jackie often wondered

how Sunny King would continue his story. She decided it probably didn't matter very much. He had that deft touch that could tug at the heart of any audience, involve them no matter what he was showing them. The pivotal strength of his movies was in the character: a hero who was human and vulnerable as well as having all the hero attributes, and a heroine one could respect and empathise with, not a stupid, clinging vine who always made silly mistakes, but someone who faced and coped with hard realities.

Jackie decided it was about time she faced up to a few hard realities. She called in a house painter to give her an estimate for painting the outside of the house. The figure he quoted horrified her, and when she questioned it he patiently explained that there was a lot of extra labour involved in scouring off the peeling paint before any new coats could be applied.

He left the itemised quotation with her. Jackie hadn't even realised that paint was so expensive. She could afford to buy that, but paying for the labour was out of the question. She and the boys would have to do it themselves, no matter how long it took them.

She borrowed a book on house painting from the library and purchased the necessary materials. At a round-table conference in the kitchen, she and the boys decided they could get one side of the house ready to paint after school hours, then paint it at the weekend. It didn't really matter how many weeks it took them. They all agreed it was better to start at the back of the house since they should be quite professional by the time they had worked around to the front.

As it turned out, they were all sick and tired of the job when they finally reached the front, but the gleaming white of the rest of the house made it look so bad in comparison that they resigned themselves to struggling on. Besides, the May vacation had begun and the boys didn't want the job hanging over their heads during the school holidays.

The tricky part was the high gable. The ladder wasn't long enough for Edmund or Robert to handle the work and Jackie herself had to reach up at full stretch. Edmund held the ladder steady while she stood on tip toe on the second-top rung.

The sudden screeching of tyres and subsequent hurtling of loose gravel almost made her teeter, and the bull-like roar of Sunny King did nothing to help her regain her balance.

'Get down! Get down from there this instant!'

For some inexplicable reason, Jackie began to shake. She leaned against the wall for support and fumbled a foot down on to the next rung of the ladder. She heard footsteps pounding across the front yard but she was too frightened to turn her head in case she fell.

'Just take it slow now, one rung at a time.' The roar had petered down into calm command. The voice came from just below her. 'If you fall I'll catch you,' it assured her.

'You startled me,' Jackie half-whimpered, then her voice gathered angry accusation as her foot found another rung and fear receded. 'I was all right until you had to do your rubber-burning act.

And you shouldn't have yelled at me like that.'

'Just shut up and get down. And why the hell are you painting the damned house? It's only fit for demolition.'

'It happens to be our home,' she yelled down at him, all her hackles rising at his high-handed denigration of their weeks of hard work.

He muttered something she couldn't quite catch but it was a mutter of some considerable feeling. And then she was back on the ground and glaring up at him and he was glaring down at her, and tears welled into Jackie's eyes because she had thought of him so much and this meeting was the very reverse of what she had planned.

'There's no point in talking to you, is there?' he growled and took the paint can from her. He flung a sharp look at Robert. 'Come over here and hold the ladder with Edmund. It'll probably shake more with my weight on it.'

He was half-way up the rungs before Jackie found her voice. 'What are you doing?' she asked stupidly.

'I'm going to paint the damned gable,' he threw at her in exasperation. 'If I don't do it, you're mad enough to go on with it as soon as my back is turned. And it's too dangerous for you.'

'But . . . but your good clothes!' For once he was conventionally dressed in a blue linen safari suit.

'I've got other clothes,' he snapped, and muttered something more about there being only one of her, thank God, whereupon he started slapping paint on to the old weatherboard with unnecessary vigour.

He was going to get paint spots all over him at that rate, Jackie thought, but held her tongue. It had finally filtered through that all his words and actions had been prompted by concern for her safety. And maybe he still cared about her.

She stood there, staring up at him, wondering how she could breach the wall of reserve between them. He was angry. There was anger in every stroke of the paint brush. Somehow she had to mollify that anger. She had caused it by frightening him and then snapping at him. She could at least try offering an olive branch, couldn't she? Even if he didn't take it, it showed good will on her part, which was more than she had ever shown him before.

He finished painting the top third of the gable and climbed down the ladder. 'Thanks, boys,' he muttered, releasing them from his command. Then he turned to Jackie, thrusting the paint tin and brush into her hands. 'Now you can get on with it without breaking your fool neck,' he gruffed dismissively.

'Thank you. It was very kind of you to help,' Jackie said meekly, not rising to his critical comment.

He shot her a sharp look and she offered him a smile. The flicker of surprise in the blue eyes encouraged her further. 'You can't get in the Lagonda with all that paint spattered on your hands and arms. Would you like to come in and clean up? It's an acrylic paint so it comes off with soap and water.'

He frowned down at his hands. 'Guess that

would be a good idea.' He lifted a carefully neutral look. 'If you don't mind.'

'Of course not. You're very welcome.' She led him in to the bathroom, very conscious of him following her down the hallway. The hairs on the back of her neck prickled. She was wearing the same shorts and T-shirt she had put on the night of his house-warming party. Did he still find her desirable?

There was no glimmer of it in his expression when she stood back to wave him into the bathroom, and, quite perversely, Jackie felt disappointed. She wanted something from him, something positive.

'I haven't had the chance to thank you for all the work you had done on my car,' she said brightly as she handed him a clean towel.

His mouth took on a sardonic curl. 'You don't owe me anything, Mrs Mulholland. I was looking after my own peace of mind.'

He was making it difficult. 'Nevertheless, I am very grateful to you. I ... I'm just going to make lunch. It's just sandwiches but if you'd like to join us ...' Oh, God! Of course he wouldn't want sandwiches, Jackie bemoaned to herself, a flush of hopeless embarrassment staining her cheeks. 'I'm not a very good housekeeper, and I suppose Mrs Willis is expecting you,' she mumbled in awkward excuse.

'No. Actually she isn't,' Sunny King said slowly.

Her eyes fluttered up to his in appeal and found a softening. 'Tomato and cheese?' she asked hopefully.

'Sounds fine.' And he smiled.

Jackie's heart flipped. She felt like skipping out to the kitchen but she forced herself to walk normally. 'Please overlook the mess. We wanted to get the painting finished so I'm a bit behind with the other work . . .' Her voice trailed away in shame at the weakness of the excuse.

'It's too much for you,' came the sympathetic comment.

'Not really. I manage most of the time,' she tossed back cheerfully, and noticed him looking around the living-room with interest.

He picked up the dinosaur on the coffee-table near the sofa and handled it curiously, a soft whimsical smile curving his mouth. He glanced up and caught her eyes on him. 'Yours?'

'Yes. It's a good selling line,' she added, glad that she hadn't brought up any llamas from the pottery shed.

'I like it. Has character,' he remarked, replacing it carefully.

'Thank you.'

He looked up and smiled again. 'You're very talented.'

'Only in a small way. Not in your class.'

His face stiffened and suspicion flashed into his eyes.

'I meant you reach millions of people with your art. I'm very small-time,' Jackie explained hastily.

He relaxed again and strolled over to her cassette collection on the shelves. 'Opera?' One eyebrow rose in quizzical disbelief. 'You like opera?'

'Love it.'

He shook his head. 'Can't stand it myself.'

The words zoomed out of her brain and almost poured of her tongue. She just clamped her mouth shut in time and, in case the urge to tell him what she thought of his ear-deafening taste in music became overwhelming, she quickly turned and moved into the kitchen.

Lots of people, most people, didn't like opera, she argued to herself as she banged a few plates down on the table and slammed the cutlery drawer. But it took someone of Sunny King's supreme arrogance to dismiss the greatest voices in the world and some of the greatest music ever written.

Jackie was aware that he had propped himself in the doorway and was watching her, but she didn't trust herself to look at him. She might be tempted to say something she might regret, although why on earth she wanted his good opinion she didn't know. They were poles apart in taste . . . nothing in common at all. They couldn't even talk for five minutes without her wanting to snap at him.

'I don't mind your liking opera though,' he declared benevolently.

Well, thank you very much, Jacke bristled. How kind of him to grant her his seal of approval! She couldn't resist a couple of shots at him. 'You should try it sometime. Open your mind to it,' she suggested sweetly.

'I have. Tried it I mean. Didn't do anything for me. But maybe I need you to show me how to enjoy it. I like your liking it. It kind of suits you.'

She felt a twinge of shame. He was being more tolerant than she was. She quelled her irritation and looked up into eyes that wanted her to like him. Shame forced a smile. 'Why do you think it suits me?' she asked, projecting light interest into her voice.

His grin held relief. 'Oh, I guess it's because you have that kind of high-tone class.'

The compliment brought a warm flush of pleasure to her cheeks even as she gave a rueful laugh. 'I don't know how you can say that after what I did to you. I was terribly wrong.'

'Trevor told me that the boys lied about having your permission to go abseiling,' he said quietly. 'I guess you were worried sick.'

He was excusing her! Jackie's flush grew painful with guilt. 'I didn't even give you the chance to tell me why you had come over that morning,' she said apologetically.

'It was just to offer you and the boys the use of the pool whenever you liked. I thought ...' He shook his head and quickly added, 'Let's forget it. Can I help you with the sandwiches? I could butter the bread.'

She needed time to regain her composure. 'No. I ... I can handle it. Would you call the boys in to wash their hands?'

'Sure,' he said good-naturedly, and went off to do her bidding.

Jackie heaved a sigh to relieve her pent-up emotion, then quickly busied herself with slicing tomatoes. If Sunny King could overlook her faults, surely she could overlook his? He was her neighbour and life would be much more pleasant if she could be friends with him. Basically he was a good, kind person and she could not look down her nose at those qualities, no matter what else he might do that irritated her.

The boys came in, obviously pleased about this apparent truce between their mother and Sunny King, and all too ready to take advantage of it.

'Have you finished the movie, Sunny?' Robert asked eagerly.

'Finished shooting it. Still some work to be done on it though.'

'When will it be coming out in the cinemas?' Edmund pressed.

'Not for a while. I won't release it until I'm fully satisfied with it.'

'Is it as good as the last?'

Pleasure rippled through Sunny King's laughter. 'I hope it's better.'

'Mum's going to come with us to see it,' Robert said in the manner of delivering the ultimate accolade to Sunny King's work.

The blue eyes shot her a questioning look.

'Yeah,' Edmund chimed in. 'She went and saw *Live By The Sword* and thought it was great. Didn't you, Mum?'

Which put her fairly and squarely on the spot, fixed by three pairs of demanding eyes. 'I enjoyed it very much,' she said lightly, aware of a self-conscious flush creeping up her neck again. She shoved a plate of sandwiches into the centre of the table to distract their attention. 'Help yourselves,' she invited, and turned away to put the electric kettle on.

'Have you put the wild kids into this one?' Robert asked.

'No. It's a completely new adventure.'

'Aw,' said Edmund, disappointed. 'I thought they were terrific.'

The whole conversation over lunch revolved around the Dirk Vescum movies and Jackie was not allowed to stand back from it. The boys continually involved her, quoting what she had said about them, forcing her into admissions. And with each admission, Sunny King's pleasure glowed a little brighter until he was fairly beaming at her, and Jackie was growing increasingly warmer under his sparkling gaze.

'I think it's time we got back to work,' she finally declared, needing some activity fast. Sunny King was eating her up with his eyes and she was terribly aware of a squirmish anticipation in herself. She had this wild fantasy of him reaching over the table for her, pulling her across it and kissing her out of her mind. And the dreadful part was, it excited her.

The boys groaned. 'Couldn't we have the rest of the day off, Mum?' Robert begged.

'We've been working like slaves,' Edmund said hopefully.

'There's not much of this first coat left to do. Let's get it finished,' Jackie insisted, and leapt up to gather the plates and put them in the sink. 'Come on now,' she said more emphatically as they lingered at the table.

Sunny stood up. 'Better do as your mother says.' He smiled at her. 'Thanks for the lunch. I really enjoyed it.'

'You're welcome,' she said as lightly as she could, and shepherded them all out to the veranda before she made an absolute fool of herself.

'I'm expecting some business calls so I have to go,' Sunny said with obvious reluctance, 'but I'll come back tomorrow and put a second coat of paint on that high part for you.'

'I ... I really can do it myself,' Jackie half-protested, a little frightened by the strength of her physical response to him. She realised now that she had been fooling herself about their becoming friends. The sexual chemistry between them would always get in the way, forcing a development she wasn't sure she could cope with.

His hand closed around her wrist in sharp emphasis. 'But you're not to do it,' he said, frowning at her. 'It's not safe.' His gaze stabbed at the boys. 'Robert, Edmund, you're not to let your mother paint the top of that gable. Agreed?'

'OK, Sunny,' Robert agreed cheerfully. 'Can Edmund and I have a ride in the Lagonda? Just along the road to your place? We'll be right back, Mum.'

Sunny King raised his eyebrows at her and she nodded, her voice completely strangled by the sensation being aroused by his hand stroking down her arm and across her wrist. Her pulse was reacting in leaps and bounds. He smiled again at her and she wondered if he knew what he was doing to her.

'See you tomorrow then,' he said in soft promise, and let her go.

The boys streaked off to get into the Lagonda

and he followed them. Jackie watched in dismay as the car roared off down the road with the usual scattering of gravel. Sunny King was just a big kid himself, lapping up praise, showing off, wanting to get his own way all the time. She was mad to have anything to do with him. It couldn't lead anywhere good.

But tomorrow couldn't come fast enough.

CHAPTER EIGHT

THE boys returned quite promptly from their ride with Sunny King and the first coat of paint was completed by mid-afternoon. Having earned their freedom, Robert and Edmund quickly disappeared on their own business. Jackie briefly wondered what they were up to, but she heard their voices in their bedroom and didn't think any more about it. There were other, more pressing matters on her mind.

She had a shower and washed her hair, then took a critical appraisal of herself in the mirror above the wash basin. She had always considered her breasts a bit on the large side, not exactly uncomfortable but more prominent than she liked. But they weren't sagging. Yet. She supposed that pummelling clay kept up the muscle tone.

She sighed over her thickened waist. Child-bearing did that to you, she told herself. It was no use expecting to look like a young girl ever again, but she didn't look too bad, considering that she had passed thirty. There were a couple of cellulite dimples on her bottom but she had always been over-endowed in that area, and he had said he liked cheeky bottoms.

He! She caught herself up on that word and dragged in a deep breath. Was she really going to

117

take the plunge and have an affair with Sunny King? That was all it could possibly be. They simply weren't compatible enough to live together in any kind of harmony. It couldn't last.

And what was she going to do when it was over? Jackie demanded of the feverish anticipation in her mirrored eyes.

Worry about that when it happens, came the voice of galloping temptation.

And what about the effect on Robert and Edmund? conscience rumbled.

Be discreet.

Huh! Sunny King wouldn't know the meaning of the word 'discreet'! He'd most likely want to flaunt his success with her in front of the whole world, just as he flaunted all his other successes in every way possible.

Jackie grabbed a bath towel, wrapped it around her treacherous body and scooted off into her bedroom to get dressed. Nudity was not conducive to sane reasoning. It was definitely insane to be considering an affair with Sunny King. Yet she definitely—well, not definitely ... But it was a terrible temptation. She had never felt like this before. With Geoff it had been more romantic. Not so ... so compelling.

She tidied up the living-room, ironed the boys' school clothes, and tried to think sensible thoughts. Without much success. She cooked tea and called the boys out of their room, hoping that their conversation would lift her mind off Sunny King.

It didn't. They were full of impressive facts about the Lagonda.

Having disposed of the hamburgers and chips Jackie had cooked, they decided to take their plates of ice-cream into the living-room so that they could watch *The Depths Of Space—How To Survive* on television. Jackie hoped it would be interesting enough to take her mind off Sunny King.

Suddenly a blinding white light flashed into the hallway. A loud sizzle like the sound of frying meat came from the boys' bedroom.

'Aw gee!' Edmund groaned. 'It's all gone up at once.'

For a moment Jackie was too stunned to move. Then she was off her chair and running down the hallway. Even before she reached the boys' door she could see fingers of flame leaping along the carpet. She turned and ran back to the kitchen for a bucket of water.

'What were you doing in your bedroom?' she screamed at the boys.

'Only a chemistry experiment,' Robert muttered, climbing to his feet to inspect the damage.

'Stay out of my way!' Jackie screeched across the kitchen counter.

Water slapped over the brim of the bucket. She dragged it out of the sink and raced for the hallway, uncaring of spillage. The heat emanating from the boys' room was suffocating. She threw the water at the door. Thick clouds of smoke rolled out, making her cough and stinging her eyes. The smell of ammonia assailed her nostrils.

Horror gripped her heart as she forced herself to look into the room. The water had had no appreciable effect upon the centre of the fire and it was already leaping up the curtains, licking around the window sill. She had no hope of stopping it. Any attempt to save the house was a waste of time. She fled back to the boys.

'Get out!' she yelled. 'Get outside immediately!'

The crackling of the old wood behind her was evidence enough of what was happening, but the boys just stood there, white-faced and shaken, staring mutely at their frantic mother. With an almighty roar the flames tore down the hallway. Jackie grabbed the boys' hands and pulled them towards the back door, her only thought being to get them to safety. The increasing roar of the fire taking hold heightened her terror. The old wood was burning like a tinder-box. Within a minute they'd be engulfed in flames.

'Run! Run for your lives!' she cried, shoving the boys ahead of her as they reached the back door.

They pelted down the yard with Jackie hard on their heels. At what she judged to be a reasonably safe distance she stopped and turned to see flames exploding out of the windows and sweeping up the newly painted walls. She swung on Robert who was panting beside her.

'What chemistry experiment were you carrying out?' she demanded.

He tore his horrified gaze from the burning house and took a frightened gulp. 'We were lighting magnesium ribbon with a candle . . . and

... and then you called us out to tea and ... and then ... something must have happened.'

'Where did you get the magnesium ribbon from?' Jackie asked in bewilderment.

'I ... er ... I nicked it from the science lab at school,' he confessed miserably.

'Oh, Robert!' She did not have the heart to say more but the sad despair in her voice reached him far more deeply than anything else she might have said.

He looked up at her with tears in his eyes and for once he had no comeback, no excuse, no defence.

'It wasn't all his fault,' Edmund cried. 'I asked him. I wanted to see. It's my fault, too. But we didn't mean it to blow up, Mum.' The tearful plea begged her forgiveness.

She automatically cuddled them both in comfort. 'I know,' she sighed. 'I know you didn't mean it.' With bleak, grieving eyes she looked back at the flaming pyre of all their possessions. Sparks were flying off the roof in the direction of the shed.

'The car!' she choked. 'We've got to save the car!' Panic drove her feet the thirty metres to the shed as she frantically yelled instructions. 'Edmund, you steer it. Robert, help me push it.' The car key was in the house. No hope of getting it. The boys raced to do her bidding.

The damned car wouldn't budge. A sob of frustration broke from Jackie's throat. She wasn't thinking clearly; the car was still in gear. Frantically she ran around to the passenger side and whipped the gear stick into neutral.

'Push when I tell you, Robert,' she cried, running back to the nearest headlight. 'Now!'

Slowly the car moved backwards. It was halfway out of the garage when the back tyres hit the slight hump on the driveway. No matter how hard they tried, they couldn't push the car beyond that hump. Tears welled into Jackie's eyes. They were going to lose everything. And she couldn't risk keeping the boys here any longer. Sparks were flying everywhere. They had to leave. Get back to safety. A car wasn't worth endangering their lives.

'Jackie! Jackie!'

Never had she been so pleased to hear Sunny King's bull-like roar. She stumbled out of the garage, exhausted from the efforts to shift the car. 'We're here!' she cried. 'We need help! We can't move it any further.'

No sooner had she finished speaking than Sunny King was there, flinging her away from the shed. 'Get your shoulder into it, Trevor!' he yelled. 'Edmund's inside. Push, Robert!'

The car literally jumped over the hump and was quickly moved to a safe distance. Before Jackie could pick herself up Sunny King was back, sweeping her into his arms and carrying her away from the shed. She glanced back over his shoulder. The whole house was totally ablaze and, with a sudden whoosh, the shed they had just left caught fire.

She groaned at the nearness of their escape and Sunny King stopped in his stride and gentled his hold on her. 'Are you hurt?' he asked anxiously.

'Did you get burnt anywhere?' He carefully lowered her feet to the ground so he could examine her for injury.

'No, I'm all right,' she assured him, but she felt faint and was glad of his support when his arms came around her and pulled her against him. She nestled her head on his shoulder, too desolated by the disaster around her to do anything but accept the comfort he offered.

It was all gone, all that she had struggled and saved for over the years, everything she and the boys had owned, all the mementoes of their lives, turning to ashes in front of her eyes. All they had left were the clothes they stood up in. And the car. The stupid car that had almost cost them their lives.

'Jackie, I swear to God I had nothing to do with this. I know I said the house was only fit for demolition, but not this way. You must believe me!'

The agonised words jabbed into her ear, forcing her head up. She looked into eyes that were dark pools of torment. Her brain was sluggish, but instinct told her how deeply he cared that she did not lay this at his door. 'I know you had nothing to with it, and I know you wouldn't ever wittingly do anything to harm anyone,' she answered softly.

He heaved a great sigh and hugged her even more tightly. 'I thought you were in there. I thought . . . Thank God you got out in time!' he muttered feverishly, his mouth moving over her hair in passionate relief.

Jackie felt too numb to care about anything until there was another explosive crack and the pottery shed burst into flame. A hoarse cry of despair burst from her throat at the realisation that the means of their livelihood was disintegrating before her eyes. Not only was the past gone, but any foothold on the future, too.

'Don't worry. I'll look after you. It'll be all right,' Sunny crooned to her over and over again as she laid her head on his shoulder and wept inconsolable tears.

'It's all my fault,' Robert said miserably.

'And mine,' Edmund sniffed.

'Trevor, take the boys home. Get Betty Willis to look after them.'

'No. We're staying with Mum,' Robert insisted, a catch of tearful emotion in his voice.

'Boys, your mother's got enough grief at the moment,' Sunny explained gently. 'Don't give her any more. Go with Trevor so she'll know you're safe. I'll bring her home with me when she's ready.'

'I'm sorry, Mum,' Robert choked out, pressing his head against her back for a brief moment.

'Me, too,' Edmund sobbed.

Jackie lifted her head to say something to them but Trevor was already leading them away and she felt too drained to resist Sunny's orders.

Cars began pulling up at the gateway, neighbours who had seen the fire and come to see if they could be of any help. It was all too evident that nothing could be saved, but they stayed on, morbidly fascinated by the disaster. Sunny kept his arm around Jackie, supporting her through the whole ordeal; answering questions, issuing orders, taking care of every contingency.

The Bushfire Brigade eventually arrived and set about putting the fire out. By the time they had finished there were only a few blackened beams left standing and a heap of debris on the ground. Beyond the smoking remains of the house stood the old brick kiln, a lone sentinel to what had once been a home.

The firemen declared the area safe and departed. The neighbours straggled off home, one by one taking sympathetic leave of Jackie. She stood there within the protective circle of Sunny King's arm, nodding dumbly to their meaningless words.

Even when they were all gone she did not move. This was her place, her home, and she stood mourning over it in hopeless grief, barely aware of the man beside her. The heat from the fire gradually dissipated on the cool night air. She began to shiver.

'Time to go,' Sunny King said gently.

She looked up at him with bleak, empty eyes. 'I have nowhere to go.'

'Yes, you have. My house is yours for as long as you want.'

She shook her head, feeling too bereft to even consider what he was offering her.

He tenderly cupped her face in his hands and forced her to meet his steady gaze. 'There are no strings attached, Jackie. Please come with me.'

A belated appreciation of the kindness and

sensitivity he had shown her tonight drove a stab of shame into her numb heart. 'Thank you for all you've done.'

His hands dropped to her upper arms, rubbing warmth into them. He spoke with urgent intensity. 'Jackie, you're in a state of shock. You must come with me. The boys are over there waiting for you. There's nothing more you can do here.'

'Yes. All right,' she got out stiffly.

His arm came around her waist, drawing her along with him as he headed towards the gateway. 'Don't worry about anything. I'll take care of you and the boys,' he assured her.

A man was standing by the Daimler, holding the back door open for them. 'The missus has got your boys safely tucked up in bed, Mrs Mulholland,' he said stoutly.

'This is Tom Willis, Jackie,' Sunny murmured.

'Thank you.' She couldn't thing of anything else to say.

Sunny bundled her into the back seat and got in after her. Tom Willis drove the Daimler down the road. Jackie felt too weary to protest when Sunny lifted her out of the car and carried her into his house. It was much easier to let herself be cradled in his arms and rest her head against his shoulder.

A middle-aged woman met them in the foyer. 'I put the electric blanket on in the turret room. I thought ...'

'That's fine. This is Betty Willis, Jackie.'

'Thank you,' she mumbled.

'Poor girl,' the housekeeper clucked. 'I put out

one of my nighties for her.'

'Good of you,' Sunny King approved. 'A cup of sweet tea, I think, Betty. And a couple of sleeping tablets.'

He took Jackie into the turret room, sat her down on the tiger bed and began to undress her. She weakly caught at his hand as his fingers flicked open the second button on her blouse.

The blue eyes bored straight into hers. 'It's all right,' he said; direct, unequivocal, nothing but help intended.

It was all right, Jackie thought vaguely. Modesty didn't matter. He had seen her before. He gently removed her blouse, slid a voluminous flannelette nightie over her head and poked her arms into the sleeves. He unbuckled her sandals and drew them off the feet, then propped her up to take off her skirt and briefs, his actions as impersonal as that of a nurse.

'Want to go to the bathroom?'

She nodded and he showed her into an en suite bathroom. She couldn't seem to manage very well. She was still at the wash basin trying to soap her hands when Sunny entered. He wiped her hands dry, picked her up and put her to bed, tucking the tiger quilt around her.

Mrs Willis came in carrying a tray. Jackie took a few sips of tea, automatically swallowed the tablets that were handed to her, then gratefully sank back down on the pillows. The bed was soft and warm. It felt good.

She had no recollection of going to sleep, nor of

dreaming, but she woke sometime during the night hearing her own voice screaming, 'Run! Run!' And another voice soothed, 'They're safe. You're all safe. You can relax. Go back to sleep.' The comfort of arms holding her safe lulled the nameless fear and it was light when she woke again.

For a few moments she felt totally disorientated. The tiger print on the tent-like curtaining brought memory flooding back. She stifled a groan, burying her face in the pillow, and only with that movement did she become aware of the arm beneath it, underneath her pillow. Slowly, carefully, with the minimum of disturbance to the bed, she turned around and stared at the man beside her.

He was still asleep, his face innocently boyish in repose, despite the golden beard. A crumpled collarless shirt clothed the top half of his body. She couldn't remember what he had worn last night but she guessed that he hadn't undressed, that he hadn't moved from her side all night. She remembered the comfort of arms cradling her when she had wakened in fear and knew he had stayed for her sake, ready to give whatever she needed. She felt humbled by all he had done for her.

'My house is yours for as long as you want.' She remembered those words. And the others, 'no strings attached'. She was sure that he had meant them sincerely at the time, but she could not fool herself into thinking that nothing would happen between them if she stayed. The attraction was there, too strong for her to resist for very long, and she couldn't possibly feel right about having an affair with him under these circumstances.

Where could she go? Her parents would take her in but that would only be under sufferance on both sides. They had more or less washed their hands of her when she had married Geoff instead of going on with the higher education they had planned for her. They would hate the disruption to their lives: she would hate depending on them. The boys would hate it even worse, being cooped up in a city town-house with no garden at all to play in.

She wondered how long it took for insurance to come through, if it was possible to get an immediate loan on the strength of it. Not that the insurance would be all that much. Not enough to build another house at today's prices. She would probably have to rent something until she could sell the land. Just the thought of doing that wrenched her heart.

She didn't want to leave here. And the truth of the matter was, she didn't want to leave Sunny King either. She didn't understand why he caused her to react so strongly—both emotionally and physically—infuriating her one minute then arousing a wild desire in her the next. Either way, she couldn't just shrug him off. He was a force she couldn't ignore or forget, and he certainly wasn't all bad, as she had first thought.

So, he liked to live in the grand manner; there was also a grandeur of soul in him that appealed to her. He valued the things she valued or he could not have created those Dirk Vescum movies. He was kind and generous, and the arrogance that she had scorned ... well, maybe he had a right to be arrogant. What other person had done what he had done?

A smile tugged at her mouth. Sunny King, the last of the great romantics. That could very well be true, she thought with a sudden will of affection, and on impulse she leaned over and kissed him.

His eyes suddenly opened, locking instantly on to hers, watchful, searching, wary. 'I thought I felt the touch of an angel,' he murmured, his voice soft and seductively musical.

The fanciful words brought a self-conscious flush to her cheeks. 'I'm sorry. I didn't mean to wake you. I shouldn't have done that.'

'As long as you're my guest you can do what you like and no harm will ever come to you.'

It was a grand gesture, so typical of the man she now knew him to be. Jackie had to smile. 'You really are a marvellous person,' she said in all sincerity. He would undoubtedly give her the shirt off his back if he thought she needed it.

'On the other hand, if you smile at me like that, I'm liable to forget my good intentions,' he warned, relief and pleasure taking any threat out of the words.

Nevertheless, Jackie dropped back on to her pillow, all too aware that now was not the time to be tempting fate. He did not follow her, except with his eyes. They were still searching hers but now with a sparkle of hope in them.

'I want you to stay with me, Jackie. Will you give it a chance?'

Live with him, he meant. In the fullest sense of the word.

'On any terms you like,' he corrected quickly. 'Just stay with me.'

But the desire for her was there in the urgency of his voice. She couldn't ignore it. 'Can I be brutally frank with you?' she asked softly.

'I'd rather you be honest,' he answered without hesitation.

Every bit of reasonable common sense she possessed told her to point out that their personalities were too different, that they would be clashing all the time, and she couldn't subject her children to the kind of tension which would inevitably develop between them if they lived together. But the look in his eyes curled around her heart, smothering common sense and forcing other words on to her tongue.

'I want to make love with you.'

The forthright admission sparked an immediate gleam of anticipation in the compelling blue eyes, and Jackie rushed out more words, panicking a little at the impulsive decision she had made. 'Not today. Today there's too much else on my mind and it wouldn't be right. But sometime, when it is right, I'm going to do that. I guess I've wanted it all along. Certainly I did last night before the fire broke out.'

'What about afterwards, Jackie?' Concern drew his eyebrows together. 'Would we still be friends or would you be bored? Disappointed?'

'I honestly don't know.' She saw the hurt her

admission gave him and quickly added, 'But I wouldn't stay here with you unless I felt there was hope for both of us . . . for being happy together.'

His face relaxed into a smile. 'You are a very remarkable woman, Jackie Mulholland.'

Jackie thought she was probably off her brain but right now she didn't care. She smiled back at him. 'And you're a very remarkable man, Mr King.'

Their smiles grew warmer with mutual satisfaction, building a sense of intimacy that had nothing to do with touching.

'What's your real name?' Jackie asked quietly. 'It can't possibly be Sunny.'

His eyebrows rose in quizzical amusement. 'You don't like Sunny?'

She wrinkled her nose at him. 'Tell me the truth.'

'Aloysius Reginald King. Take your pick,' he invited with an open grin.

'You're not kidding me?'

'That's what's on my birth certificate. I can show it to you.'

She sighed. 'I guess I'll get used to Sunny.'

He gathered her up and pulled her over his chest, his eyes laughing up at her. 'It's how you make me feel, all bright and warm and sparkly.'

Which was how she was feeling, too, despite having lost everything she had ever owned. 'I'd better get up and see to the boys.'

'See to a lot of things,' he agreed happily. He kissed her on the nose, rolled her back to her pillow, tossed the bedclothes aside and fairly leapt to his feet in a burst of energy. 'I must get in touch with my architect straight away,' he announced. 'Have to start building again.'

'Building what?' she asked, feeling an apprehensive tingle in her spine. 'Sunny, I can't afford to ...'

'I'm not going to have you bored. We're going to build the best pottery workroom that any potter ever had. Every kind of kiln ...'

'No. No!'

'Then the house ...'

'Stop it, Sunny! You're taking over again.'

It was as if he hadn't heard her. '... We'll build it on a scale that will leave the world bemused,' he burbled on, totally enthralled with his own ideas.

'Stop thinking like that at once!' Jackie shrilled at him. 'I can't afford it! I can't!'

'Don't worry about money. I've got money to burn,' he declared happily. 'Who's the best architect?'

'We don't need ...'

'Joern Utzon! He designed the Sydney Opera House. That's who we'll get. I'll build you the house of your dreams. Everything you've ever ...'

'There's nothing wrong with this house!' she cried in panicky protest.

He frowned at her. 'You don't like it. You said it was dreadful.' The frown disappeared into blissful enthusiasm. 'We'll have the ultimate in elegance, the ...'

'I like this house!' Jackie insisted wildly. 'I love it. It's a great house.'

'Stop interrupting me. I have this vision . . .'

'Sunny!'

'All those house plans are still in my study.'
Excitement beamed at her. 'I'll be right back with
your clothes. Betty took them off to launder them
last night. Ah, we're going to have a marvellous
day,' he threw at her exultantly and was out of the
door before Jackie could find any retort at all.

She slumped back on her pillow and rolled her
eyes. Well, she'd made her bed. This was it. It
wasn't as if she hadn't known that Sunny King was
uncontrollably mad. Besides, it might turn out to
be marvellous. All she had to do was bend a little.
Maybe a lot. But if Sunny King was mad, it was in a
beautiful, beautiful way. And she had no regrets at
all about her decision. Not yet anyway.

CHAPTER NINE

WELL, she certainly hadn't been bored, Jackie reflected, as she drove her old Datsun towards St Alban's. Frustrated, exasperated, and debilitated by Sunny's unstoppable dynamism, yes ... but never bored.

Sometimes she thought she was living with a brick wall, and, no matter how much she battered her head against it, it seemed impervious. Then, suddenly, unpredictably, it gave way, only to reappear from another direction.

Like the clothes. She had won the battle of the clothes and paid for them herself, establishing some independence from Sunny's compulsive generosity. She hadn't been able to buy much, apart from re-fitting the boys for school and a few necessary items for herself, but it was enough to go on with until the money came through from the insurance. However, while she was buying clothes, Sunny was off buying compact discs of all the greatest operas ever recorded. Hundreds and hundreds of dollars worth of music, just for her.

'Please send them back,' she had begged.

'Everyone's entitled to enjoy their own kind of music. Food for the soul. Isn't that what they say? I wouldn't be looking after you properly if you didn't have food for your soul,' was the solemn reply.

'Sunny, I don't want you spending a lot of money on me,' she had insisted.

He had looked hurt. 'But that's my pleasure.'

She had dug her toes in. 'I won't play them. You have to send them back.'

'No. I'm not going to have you getting bored,' was his final line on the argument and the box of discs was still sitting in her room.

Then came the trail-bikes for Robert and Edmund. It had been very hard to argue with Sunny in the face of the boys' delirious joy, but she had tried. 'Boys have to have trail-bikes,' he had growled. 'Otherwise they're not boys.'

It didn't matter how much she protested, somehow he defeated her. How did one fight against a man whose pleasure was in giving pleasure? His eyes sparkled excitement and happiness at her and she ended up weak-kneed. And of course, the boys thought he was marvellous. Which he was.

But Jackie didn't like the feeling of being steamrollered all the time. The years of careful planning and budgeting had instilled a caution in her that was continually appalled by Sunny's extravagance. She wasn't even sure that he had shelved the idea of designing her a new house, although she had done her best to convince him that she couldn't possibly afford it. He didn't seem to understand that concept at all.

Or didn't want to. He refused to accept any

contribution from her towards their keep and
Jackie was beginning to feel quite stressed by the
situation. She couldn't just stay on indefinitely,
accepting his largesse. On the other hand, she
didn't want to leave him. She wished she had her
old house back, then she could still enjoy a
relationship with him without feeling so damned
beholden to him.

There was not one day that passed that Sunny
didn't put her in some emotional dilemma. Like
this morning. 'Since you're only going into the city
to finalise this insurance business, and you don't
like me buying you things, I think I'll stay at
home,' he had declared, but Jackie was accustomed
to spotting evasion on Robert's and Edmund's
faces, and she saw that same shiftiness on Sunny's.

'Oh? What are you going to do here?' she had
asked, pretending to be disappointed.

Sunny had a moment's pause, then his face had
lit up. 'Robert and Edmund need to be taught the
finer points of safe riding on their trail-bikes.'

'You? Teach them safe riding?' she had choked.
It was madness. Sunny was worse than the boys.

'Yes. Things like how to ride out of a skid and
what to do if you're going to fall. Very important to
know things like that. Save them from injury.'

How could she argue against that? But if they
were still all in one piece by the time she arrived
back, it would be the world's eighth wonder. And
Sunny had looked overly pleased with her compliance. He really was worse than the boys. She
couldn't trust him out of her sight not to get up to

some kind of mischief.

Jackie came over the crest of the last hill on the home stretch and Sunny's latest bit of mischief was right in front of her eyes. She slammed on the brakes, parked on the side of the road, and gaped at the biggest bulldozer she had ever seen. It was making a last sweep through the remnants of her house. The old brick kiln was gone. A traxcavator was shovelling up the last of the blackened bricks and dumping them into the back of a waiting truck. Jackie got out of the car and walked over to the new fence in a daze.

The fence is the first to go . . .

Then the kiln and the ramshackle sheds . . .

Then the house . . .

And then you. I'm going to take you under my wing and give you all you deserve.

Those had been Sunny's words, as well as she could remember them, and here it was . . . all done . . . except the final surrender from her. And that was only a matter of time now that she was living under his roof. Sunny had not pressured her to go to bed with him. He seemed content to wait until she was ready, and Jackie knew in her heart that it was inevitable. In fact, the closer the inevitable came, the more appeal it seemed to have.

With a strange bittersweet sadness, Jackie had to acknowledge that Sunny had been right about her old home messing up his view. Now that everything had been razed to the ground, she could see that the area was much prettier with just countryside all around Sunny's house. Even his monstrosity of a house seemed right, its turrets poking up to the sky like a small medieval castle, lord and master of all it surveyed.

A little smile played around her mouth. It was crazy but she was beginning to like Sunny's house. She no longer thought of her tiger-room as grotesque. It was like a sumptuous, romantic fantasy and she enjoyed waking up in it, luxuriating in the sensual opulence of all the furnishings. It was the kind of room that no one but Sunny King would dare to have, but wasn't it what everyone secretly wished to experience at least once in a lifetime?

And really, the whole house was like that. Like Sunny himself. Grandeur run riot. Totally uninhibited. And it was fun. Jackie even had to admit to occasionally pretending she was one of those old-time movie actresses making a grand entrance as she walked down the curved staircase.

But is wasn't her home, and she had to start making some definite plan about the future. The house insurance was not enough to build again. Maybe if she took from the capital of Geoff's life insurance ... But if she did that, could she make enough pottery for them to live on? The sensible thing to do would be to sell the land, which she knew would fetch a high price. Except that that meant moving away.

She climbed back into her car and drove on up to Sunny's driveway, having resolved nothing. As she entered the house, Sunny came bounding up the staircase from his study, his expression an odd mixture of anxiety and pleasurable anticipation. 'I've got something to show you!' he exclaimed, somewhat unnecessarily, his eyes darting warily over her expression.

'I see you got rid of the eyesore,' she said in dry resignation.

'It was dangerous, Jackie,' he said slowly, measuring her attitude as he spoke. 'The boys were poking around over there the other day. I thought I'd better send the bulldozer in. Save them from any harm.'

She had to smile. If there was a way around anything she was sure Sunny would find it. 'There couldn't be a better reason than that,' she said with warm approval.

Surprise and relief chased over his face. 'You're not mad with me?'

'You said you were going to do it. Now I don't have to worry any more about when you're going to do it. And it does look much better,' she assured him.

His arms came around her in an exuberant hug. 'You are really starting to think like a sensible woman,' he breathed happily.

But it was the look in his eyes that tripped Jackie's heartbeat. She had only seen it once before in her life—when Geoff had asked her to marry him. And here it was again, compelling, binding, *loving*. Love, showering from his brilliant blue eyes in actinic rays. It staggered Jackie out of her mind, but she could not possibly doubt it.

Sunny King loved her. And it explained everything that had happened: why he was so good to her, so kind, so considerate. In one intense moment of humility Jackie vowed that she would never again do anything to hurt this man, even if she had to bite her tongue off.

'Come on down to my study,' he urged. 'There's someone I want you to meet and something I want you to see.'

He swept her along with him while Jackie was still mentally swept off her feet by the knowledge she had just acquired. A tall thin man with a long face was behind Sunny's desk and he nodded indulgently at her as Sunny performed introductions.

'Jackie, this is my architect, Jason Guthrie.'

Architect! Oh, no! No, no, no, her mind cried. 'Sunny, I don't want another house. If I want to build another house I'll do it myself. But I rather think I might buy somewhere else. I don't know yet what I'll do,' she pleaded anxiously.

He laughed and dropped a kiss on her forehead. 'It's not a house. Just a little pottery workshop. When I knocked your kiln down I certainly wasn't intending that you should do without one. Jason's drawn up some plans that I want you to look at very closely. They're very clever but they're still only preliminary sketches and you've got to tell him where he's gone wrong so he can get it exactly right. Precisely what you want and need.'

'That's right,' Jason Guthrie chimed in. 'We can do it any number of ways. The aim is to have it exactly right for you.'

She couldn't keep taking from Sunny King. It was parasitic. He saw the quandary of conscience in her eyes and immediately launched into persuasive appeal. 'Jackie, an artist of your creativity deserves the best. How can you do your works of genius if . . .'

'But I . . .' She couldn't accept it but she didn't want to hurt Sunny, either. Nor put him down in front of his architect. 'This is too much. I'm not a very good potter, Sunny. Really I'm not.'

He whipped around, picked some object off a shelf and held it out to her, his eyes sparkling with teasing humour. It nestled in the palm of his hand, and the awful recognition of her own handicraft sent Jackie into a paralytic shock. 'Anyone who can create something as magnificent as this can't be kept from her work,' Sunny declared triumphantly.

It was one of the llamas that Jackie had baked with such terrible animosity in her heart. Sunny King's face was immediately recognisable. Shame flooded through her. She peered up at him guiltily through half-lowered lashes. 'Sunny, I . . . I'm so sorry, I . . .'

'I'm not,' he chuckled. 'Best thing I've ever seen. One day it'll be a collector's piece. I'm buying all I can get my hands on. Give them to my friends as Christmas gifts. Now come and cast your eye over Jason's plans.'

Absolutely mortified by Sunny's pleasure in the llama, Jackie tamely acceded to his wishes. The workshop Jason Guthrie had sketched was any potter's dream. She nodded like an automaton as he explained the efficient grouping of the kilns and work benches, the shelf storage and every other thoughtful detail. Sunny beamed at her approval. He gave Jason Guthrie the go-ahead and the architect departed.

Jackie could not let the matter pass. She was consumed with guilt. As soon as they were alone she turned to Sunny in abject apology. 'It was wicked of me to put your face on those llamas.'

He grinned from ear to ear. 'They're certainly wicked.'

'Why aren't you mad at me?' she asked in bewilderment, then knew it was a stupid question. She knew the answer. He loved her.

His face softened as he drew her into a gently comforting embrace. 'Because when I found them, it was the first time I felt confident of success. That wickedly executed face meant I'd really got through to you. I have, haven't I?'

A self-conscious laugh gurgled up her throat. 'You're not wrong.' Then a flood of feeling that she did not stop to analyse made her reach up and wind her arms around his neck. 'Remember that first night when you wanted to show me your bedhead from Bali and I refused to look at it?'

'I remember it well,' he said. There was a deep note of longing in his voice.

'I'd like to see it now, Sunny,' she said softly.

The hands that had begun to gather her closer were suddenly still. His whole body held an unnatural stillness as his eyes searched hers. 'Not because of some mistaken sense of gratitude, Jackie,' he said as though forcing the words out, and the necessity for them hurt.

It was true that she wanted to give him what he desired, but not only because he had given her so much. There was no hesitation over her reply. 'It would never be for that reason, Sunny, I promise you. And I'm old enough to know my own mind.'

'Would you ever come to love me?'

The question carried a note of pleading and there was no easy answer this time. She reached up and kissed him. 'Believe me, I wouldn't want it . . . you . . . if I didn't feel . . . if I didn't want you, Sunny. I think there is a great chance of it working out right.'

A flicker of disappointment was instantly wiped out by warm optimism. 'It will be all right,' he declared. 'It has to be,' he muttered half under his breath as he turned her to walk with him.

It was strange, because she knew she wanted him, wanted to know him in the most intimate way of all, yet now that the moment of decision had come, Jackie felt increasingly nervous with each step they took towards his bedroom. She had never had sex with anyone apart from Geoff, and she probably wasn't very good at it anyway. Certainly not a match for a man of Sunny's experience. What if she failed to live up to his expectations? What if he was bored with her afterwards?

Sunny closed the bedroom door softly behind them. Apparently he was in no hurry, for he leaned back against the door, his hand gently holding hers.

She shot him a tense, apprehensive look and with a soft laugh he shook his head at her. 'You look like the kid who was caught stealing the apple.'

'More like Eve caught by Adam,' she retorted, giving vent to some of her pent-up emotion.

His smile offered her understanding. 'You have every right to be apprehensive, but I don't want you to be. Come here.' He gently tugged her hand and she took the step back to him. His arms slid around her. 'Hug me. Just be close to me,' he softly urged. 'I'll understand. I certainly won't have you doing anything you don't want to do.'

It was a relief to accept his embrace, to slide her arms around him and press into the warmth and strength of his body. It felt good, as if she belonged there. His hand ruffled through her hair, soothing, caressing, loving. There was no urging, no haste. He gave the impression of being content to stand there all day, for all the days of his life, just holding her.

She raised her head and his lips brushed lightly over hers, leaving and coming back in a slow, continual searching out of her response, ridding her of her inhibitions by never offering more than she wanted to receive, was eager to receive and give back.

She could never remember making love to Geoff except in the dark. It had been that kind of relationship, matter-of-fact rather than this delib- erate incitement and enjoyment of sensuality. She did not think that Sunny would ever feel a need for darkness in order to give his love.

His fingers glided down her back, found nerve-endings that made her shiver with pleasure, yet still they felt incredibly soft, their contact not really firm, simply more intimate. His hand trailed slowly from her hair, across her neck, down her throat, stroking her skin softly to the top button of her blouse.

'It's all right, Jackie,' he whispered into her ear. 'I've seen how you look before . . . lovely, womanly, beautiful . . .'

Her mouth blindly sought his, wanting, needing its comfort, its reassurance, its excitement. And he answered her need with a sensitivity that completely drowned any possible apprehension.

The buttons were undone one by one, each a deliberate movement denying any thought of taking a sly advantage, almost a waiting for assurance of her consent. Then her blouse was opened, pushed gently from her arms, and it felt marvellous to press her naked breasts against him.

She wondered if she should be doing something, touching him, undoing his shirt, but when Sunny's hands came up to perform that operation himself, it seemed better to let their touch brush down the exquisite sensitivity of her bare flesh. It was even better when she was pressed against the warm smoothness of his naked chest.

He cradled her in his arms, rocking her gently as though she were a child, loving her with a tenderness that none the less held a soft, exciting yearning, a need to belong, to have and to hold, to possess. Jackie threw her arms around his neck to cling even closer. Never had she felt such exciting anticipation, such feverish desire.

His hands undid her skirt and pushed the material down over her broad, firm hips, collecting her briefs on the way; Jackie stepped out of them, a slow deliberate step. She knew that she would not have done this for any other man.

Sunny picked her up effortlessly and carried her towards the bed, his lips playing a symphony of longing and desire over her own. He opened the curtaining on the four-poster with a sweep of one hand and gently laid her down. He stood over her, dominant, commanding, his eyes luminous with passionate desire for her as he stripped off what was left of his clothes. It was done without haste, with an arrogant assurance that she would not change her mind now.

The way his eyes lingered on her, examining her in the minutest detail, was too much for Jackie, filling her with a melting heat that almost made her squirm. She stretched out her hand to him. 'Please ...' Her voice sounded furry, almost unrecognisable.

He sat down next to her, his hands lightly caressing erotic areas, awakening an exquisite sensitivity to his touch. His head lowered over her, his mouth tracing the path of his hands, and Jackie gasped with each new contact, each delicate nuance and sharp wave of pleasure. Her body was exploding with vibrant sensations, nerve-endings quivering with fierce delight, her arms and legs aching from the melting weakness spreading through them.

Sunny's body moved sensuously over her own. She was going out of her mind with the need for a resolution to the feelings he had aroused. Her hands were running around the solidity of his chest, scrabbling over the thickly muscled shoulders, raking down his back. He groaned. She thought wildly that she should apologise, but he moved his body to touch hers intimately, urgently, and all thought fled from her mind as the muscles in her thighs went entirely limp, quivering helplessly as he gently spread her legs apart to admit him.

When he entered her body she moved with him, completely abandoning herself to the rhythm of his making, wanting only to follow where he led, wanting him to do with her as he pleased, pleasing her with the pulsing strength of his desire.

His movements were slow and exquisite, a delicate almost torturous preliminary to a passion that gradually built to a wild pounding of satyric pleasure. Jackie lost all control, her body a helpless vessel that spasmed with ecstatic pleasure as he plunged into her, his possession, and her total surrender of self to his pleasure drove him wild. She heard him crying out, felt the urgent, jerking thrusts that strove for the ultimate climax, knew a primitive exultation at the driving power of his need, received him with a searing tenderness when he finally collapsed on her, his breath coming in hoarse gasps, his heart pounding its strained distress.

She sighed her contentment, at peace with the world and all that was in it. She glided her hands over his back, caressing and soothing, happy to give him the comfort he had given her. His arms hugged her tightly to him. His legs wound around hers, twining and intertwining as they moved languorously over the bed, shifting contacts, fingers and toes meeting, moving, melting together, savouring their togetherness. Never had after-sex felt so wonderfully close, so deliciously sensual, so gloriously right.

'Feel good?' Sunny murmured, nuzzling her ear to her squirming delight.

'Mmm.' She moved her foot up the calf of his leg. Fingers grazed teasingly over her sole and she laughed as she quickly stroked her foot down again. 'I'm not so sure about your bedhead, but you're a master craftsman, Sunny King.'

He gave a soft chuckle. 'I've never felt better in my life. We were made for each other, Jackie Mulholland.'

They lay there a long time, savouring their contentment. Then Sunny abruptly moved, shifting himself to rest on his side, his head propped up with one hand, eyes twinkling with sheer devilment as he gazed down at the placid satisfaction on her face.

'What are you thinking?' Jackie asked.

'I was wondering if it was possible to be any happier than I am now.'

'And what conclusion did you come to?'

Jackie squeaked at the provocative glide of his hand up her thigh. The look in his eyes grew alarmingly purposeful.

'I'm not going to die wondering about it,' he murmured into her ear.

And it didn't take very long at all to convince Jackie that she shouldn't die wondering about it either. What he was doing was absolutely right.

CHAPTER TEN

'CAN we go abseiling with Trevor, Mum?'
Edmund blurted out over breakfast, earning a swift
kick under the table from his elder brother.

Robert immediately put on his appeasing face.
'Not really abseiling, Mum. More like bush-
walking, only we'll have ropes and things with us to
make sure we're safe wherever we go and whatever
happens.'

Jackie cut straight through the palaver. 'The
answer is absolutely no. You are not going with
Trevor under any circumstances, so you might as
well forget it right now.' She fixed Trevor with a
stern look of warning.

'Not my idea, Mrs Mulholland,' he said with a
dismissive shrug. 'The boys asked me and I told
them they had to ask you. In my hearing,' he added
with an 'I told you so' look at the intrepid
petitioners.

'Thank you, Trevor,' Jackie said with warm
approval.

He was a trustworthy young man, she decided,
which was probably why Sunny had hired him as
his personal assistant. She was beginning to have a
very healthy respect for Sunny's judgement of
character. Betty Willis was a marvellously efficient
and cheerful housekeeper, and her husband, Tom,

was equally hard-working and always seemed to be available to lend a helping hand with anything.

Betty came in to clear the table and the boys stood up and helpfully gathered up their own used plates. 'We'll go for a ride on our bikes down the road,' Robert announced casually. 'If that's all right, Mum?'

'Yes,' she nodded, thankful that they hadn't decided to be argumentative. She had too big a problem on her mind to suffer being pestered by the boys. 'But be careful,' she added warningly. 'And take jumpers with you. It's cold today and it'll be even colder on a bike.' Although it was only the third week in May, the cold blustering winds outside announced that winter was definitely on its way.

'Could we take some fruit with us, Mrs Willis?' Edmund asked chirpily. 'In case we get hungry?'

'Of course you can,' Mrs Willis agreed, smiling indulgently at both boys. 'And there are cookies in the tin. I baked them specially for you yesterday.'

'Gee, thanks, Mrs Willis. You're a terrific cook,' Robert declared, pouring on the charm. 'Really great at cookies and cakes!'

Crawler, Jackie thought with a sudden appreciation of his potential with the ladies when he grew older. He had Betty Willis eating out of his hands already, and Edmund was learning fast. The kindly housekeeper would spoil them rotten if Jackie didn't keep a watchful eye on proceedings.

Though really, the boys hadn't given her any reason for complaint since they had burnt the house down. Their behaviour had been admirable, which had probably placed an almost intolerable strain on their systems. There was only one more day to go before the new school term began and so long as they didn't manage to kill themselves on their bikes before Monday she was hopeful of relative peace for some time to come. Her only immediate problem was her relationship with Sunny. She had to find out what was wrong.

A covert glance at him showed her he was wearing that distracted look again. She doubted that he had heard one word spoken over the table this morning. He was brooding over something and it was beginning to get to her. His mood had been very much less than sunny for the last couple of days.

Was he bored with her now that she had given in to him? It worried Jackie. Didn't he want her here any more? Suddenly he stood up, excused himself from the table and headed off without one personal word to her. Jackie realised she found it more than worrying.

She looked over at Trevor, needing some hint of what was wrong, because something definitely was. If Sunny was disappointed in their relationship she couldn't hang on here, no matter how reluctant she felt to leave him. 'Do you know what's worrying Sunny, Trevor?'

'I ... er ... don't think it's for me to say, Mrs Mulholland. You'll have to ask Sunny,' he finished in a mumble, his eyes evading her direct gaze. He immediately pushed himself to his feet and excused himself to go and catch up on some overdue paperwork.

Jackie was left alone and she felt utterly miserable, shut off and unwanted. She trailed off to the laundry to do some washing. There was nothing else for her to do around the house since Mrs Willis reigned in the kitchen and two cleaning ladies came in every day to keep the place spick and span.

Her mind fretted over the problem with Sunny. Something was definitely wrong and she felt deeply hurt that he chose not to discuss it with her. She wanted to share more than her bed with him. Their relationship was too one-sided. Sunny gave her everything he possibly could, and she was unable to reciprocate except with the pleasure she gave him when they made love.

Somehow that seemed insignificant now. Since he wasn't communicating with her in any other way, he obviously thought she couldn't supply whatever it was he needed. It made her feel totally inadequate. And the possibility that she might be losing him made her feel even worse. She decided she would have to get to the root of the problem but was undecided on how best to go about it.

She filled in the morning trying out sketches for future creations in clay, but her mind wasn't on the task. Sunny didn't even appear for lunch and Mrs Willis informed her that he had been down in the theatre all morning and had told her he didn't want to be disturbed. Disappointment acted as a spur and Jackie decided she had to take the bull by the horns. She made up a plateful of sandwiches and took it down to the theatre.

She gave a courtesy knock on the door, then opened it quickly before Sunny had a chance to tell her to go away. She caught the familiar face of Dirk Vescum on the screen before she spotted Sunny hunched over on the far sofa, his head in his hands, not even watching the movie, obviously not aware of her entrance either. She walked over to him, the thick carpet muffling her footsteps. She had to touch him to draw his attention.

Sunny's head jerked up. On the instant of recognition his hand flashed to the table for the remote control. The screen blanked out and the overhead light blinked on. 'Jackie?' The vaguely quizzical note in his voice told her she had interrupted a deep concentration and it was clearly a struggle for him to bring his mind to bear on her unexpected appearance.

A sense of guilt frayed her confidence but the damage was done now. She was here with him and she had to speak up. 'I thought you might like some lunch. And I wanted to talk to you.' She set the plate of sandwiches on the table in front of him and tried an encouraging smile.

'Something wrong?' he asked, making Jackie realise that she usually only sought him out to voice some frustration or other. She suddenly felt ashamed of how self-centred she had been.

'What's wrong with us, Sunny? What's wrong with me?' she blurted out without any preamble.

He looked astonished. 'How can you think such a

thing? There's nothing wrong with you. You're perfect,' he insisted staunchly.

'But you're not happy.'

'I am. I couldn't be more so.'

'No, you're not. You've been brooding over something for days. Please tell me the truth.'

Her obvious distress caused him to pause and frown. Still frowning he shot her a guarded look. 'It's the movie. It's not right and I don't know how to fix it.' The admission was reluctant and clearly painful to him.

'Tell me about it,' she asked quietly.

He shook his head. 'I'll work it out eventually.'

With a flash of insight, Jackie remembered how unfair she had been in her criticism of his movies before she had seen them. If Sunny didn't think the movie was right, then he would be wary of her opinion. She had hurt him in her blind prejudice and might hurt him again. Where she was concerned he was particularly vulnerable. He wanted her approval, her admiration. It would be going against his grain to admit anything that he would consider a failure on his part.

'Please, Sunny, won't you let me share this with you?' she begged, and was surprised at the urgent need in her voice.

It surprised him, too. His eyes focused sharply on her, questioning. 'I don't want to bore you, Jackie. You can't really care about . . .'

'I care about you,' she interrupted softly, and it was true. She really did care about what he thought and felt.

A warm, happy glow lit Sunny's eyes and he took her hand and drew her down on to his lap. He smiled as she uninhibitedly threw her arms around his neck and snuggled closer. Then he kissed her and his hand closed softly over one breast.

Jackie sucked in a deep, determined breath and pulled his hand away. 'Not now, Sunny,' she told him firmly.

'No?' His eyebrows arched in provocative disbelief.

'I can't think when you do that, and I need to share everything with you. Lovemaking isn't enough. It never would be.'

'But there's nothing I like better than making love to you,' he argued, placing persuasive little kisses around her face.

'Please, don't cut me off.'

He sighed and surrendered. 'You're right.' He fell into brooding again for a long time before he continued. 'The truth is I'm satisfied with the movie. That's not the problem. It's the music. It's just not doing what I want it to do and I can't figure out what it needs. All I know is that it's wrong.'

The confession really pained him. Jackie could feel the hurt emanating from him with every word he had forced out. She wondered if this was the first time he had ever confessed to failure. If so, it was a very big thing he had done for her.

'Show me the movie, Sunny,' she urged softly. 'Let me hear how it sounds. I'd like to see what you've done, anyway. Then we can talk about it.'

He hesitated, obviously not liking her to see the

imperfect product, then he took in the sincere appeal in her eyes and shrugged. 'If that's what you want.'

He sat her on the sofa and reset the tape of the movie back to its beginning. Jackie kicked off her sandals and settled herself comfortably next to him, preparing for a long session of full concentration. She was not about to criticise his failing at something. What really mattered was being allowed to share his failures as well as his successes. Sunny threw her a half-wary, vulnerable look; then, with a resigned sigh, he pressed the appropriate buttons on his remote control panel.

The movie was entitled *Strike At The Heart* and from the very opening scene Jackie was enthralled with it. The story revolved around the plan for the ultimate destruction of the aliens' headquarters. Dirk Vescum showed his love for Alena by becoming more and more protective of her. At one particularly desperate part of the action, Dirk's forces were being annihilated when Alena arrived to join him. His despair at seeing her was written over his face as he fiercely rejected her support, and her love for him was equally moving as she fiercely counter-challenged him with the steely words, 'Do you think I would want to live without you?'

The fighting action that followed was hectic edge-of-the-seat stuff that had Jackie's heart in her mouth all the way until the final resolution. She was barely aware of the music until the climax of the battle. The aliens' headquarters was being bombarded—explosions, fire, chaos everywhere—

and then she knew exactly what Sunny meant. The action was spectacular. It cried out for a spectacular burst of music to highlight it and generate the feeling of awesome triumph. Something tremendously climactic. And what was there was wrong.

'Play that last part again, Sunny,' she asked as the movie ended. She was almost sure she knew what was needed.

Sunny groaned in despair. 'It's hopeless, isn't it? I'll have to get another composer. Another score. But how to tell them what I want when I don't know myself? That's the hell of it.'

Impelled by his pained outburst to offer solace, Jackie didn't hesitate any longer. 'Sunny, the music you need . . . I think it might already have been written.' She jumped to her feet in excitement. 'Wait here! I'll be right back. I think I've got what you want,' she babbled and was off before he could say a word.

She raced up the stairs to her room and tore open the box of compact discs that Sunny had bought her. She had stubbornly refused to play them and he had stubbornly refused to send them back. She sorted through them in purposeful haste and triumphantly pounced on the recordings she was looking for, Wagner's *Götterdämmerung*—Twilight of the Gods—the final opera of the *Ring* quartet, and *The Ride of the Valkyries*. If Sunny couldn't see how this music fitted his concept then he was a . . . a troglodyte. She skipped back down the stairs to the theatre.

'Can we play the compact discs in here?' she cried excitedly.

'What have you got?' Sunny asked, eyes suspicious at her enthusiasm.

'The music, of course! You'll have to be patient with me while I find the exact places on the discs. Then I'll play the music for you while you play the climax of the movie without any other sound. Then you'll see.'

He shook his head, somewhat bemused, but he helped her to the necessary equipment and waited, watching her with quizzical eyes until she found what she wanted. At her direction he rewound the film to the critical point where the music had failed to grab the essence of the action.

'Now watch and listen,' she commanded, hoping he would see what she was trying to show him.

In unison they pressed the necessary controls. The mighty music of Wagner swelled into the room in crashing waves, building with huge dramatic force towards its magnificent, thunderous climax, evoking the awesome image of Valhalla in flames, of Valhalla falling, of Valhalla being destroyed.

After that she instantly switched to *The Ride of the Valkyries*, with its soaring chords of triumph. To Jackie these pieces of music were amongst the most soul-stirring ever composed and she was certain that their sheer grandeur would have to appeal to Sunny. She was right. He sat through it absolutely mesmerised, watching his film, hearing the music.

Only when the last note echoed into silence did he bounce up, rubbing his hands together in exultant glee. 'Do that to me again!' he commanded.

She played the music over and over. They tried to synchronise the action to the music a little better and Sunny was sparkling with elation at the effect produced. He grabbed Jackie and whirled her around.

'I've got it! I've got it! I knew I could do it, you marvellous woman!' he cried, giving her an exuberant hug before putting her down so he could pace around in a fever of excitement. 'I can see it now. That's the material to use. We'll jazz it up. Make it really big. Use three orchestras. Intersperse it with a rock band. I know exactly how to do it now.'

A rock band! Intersperse Wagner's great music with a rock band! All Jackie's delight at providing the answer to Sunny's problem was instantly crushed by a mountain of horror, quickly followed by a tidal wave of furious indignation. Her mouth opened. Her brain tossed around venomous words. Her voice lifted to shrilling pitch.

'You phil ...'

Sunny turned to her, his face still alight with happy triumph. Her mouth bit down on her tongue, cutting off the word, philistine, in mid-shrill. Her brain abruptly changed gears and whirled again. Hadn't she wanted to make him happy? And what right did she have to be so arrogant in her judgements?

You need a bit of humility, Jackie Mulholland, she warned herself. You're not always right. Sunny King had proved time and time again that he knew what he was doing when he was making movies for the market. Horses for courses, she reminded herself fiercely.

Sunny frowned at her tightly clamped mouth. 'What did you say I was?' he asked warily.

Jackie put on a belated smile. 'A philomel,' she replied with lilting innocence. Sometimes it was really useful to have a good vocabulary.

Sunny's responding smile held an uncertain tilt. 'What does that mean?'

She waltzed up to him and hung her arms around his neck, her eyes softly teasing him. 'Oh, somebody who makes music like a nightingale. Like you.'

The elation came back in a delighted grin. 'Jackie, you're the most wonderful woman in the whole world. I knew my instincts were right when I first saw you, sleeping in the moonlight on the veranda. I knew then you had to be mine. And I was right.'

For some reason the blatant arrogance of that speech didn't matter because the love in his eyes more than made up for it, and when he kissed her she was very, very glad that she had held her tongue, because the sweet hunger of his kiss was far more satisfying than any amount of intellectual pride.

'Mum! Mum!'

The urgent cries broke them apart as Edmund

burst into the room, his small face white and terrified.

'Robert's caught below a ledge. I couldn't pull him up. The ropes have knotted on the overhang. I tried and tried,' he panted out in hopeless distress.

'My God! You went abseiling!' Jackie cried, her heart cramping with fear even as she made the accusation.

'Where is he, Edmund?' Sunny snapped out.

'Up the mountain at the end of the road. Where Trevor took us the last time,' Edmund replied.

'I told you not . . .' Jackie began, despair adding its bite to her heart.

'We didn't! You told us not to go with Trevor, so we went by ourselves. Robert figured . . .'

'No time for that,' Sunny whipped in. 'It's cold outside and it'll be dark soon. We've got to move.'

And he was off, yelling out for Trevor, roaring orders. 'Alert the Police Rescue Squad. Get an ambulance. And the Westpac Rescue Helicopter. Anybody else who can help. Betty, bring blankets to the Range Rover. And Tom, you bring ropes and torches. The big spotlights.'

Before she had time to think Jackie was pushed into the Range Rover. Sunny King slammed the four-wheel drive vehicle into gear and pressed the accelerator flat to the floor. For once, Jackie had no criticism of his propensity for speed.

She looked anxiously at the sky. The afternoon had slipped away while she and Sunny had been down in the theatre. At most there would only be an hour left before darkness fell. A bitterly cold wind had blown up. Robert had already been under that unprotected ledge, hanging suspended in mid-air, for over two and a half hours.

She turned to Edmund who was huddled on the back seat of the Range Rover. 'Has Robert got his jumper on?'

Edmund shook his head miserably. 'We took them off and left them on the top of the cliff before he went down. I tried to throw it to him, Mum, but I threw it too far out and he couldn't catch it. And the same thing happened with my own.'

The clutch of fear deepened. If they couldn't haul Robert up, if he had to stay there overnight . . . Geoff had died like that, hanging in mid-air, frozen to death before anyone could help.

A warm hand clasped her knee. She darted a distracted look at Sunny. 'We'll make it there before dark. We'll get him up. No point in thinking negative thoughts, Jackie,' he said quietly.

'No,' she agreed shakily, and breathed a silent prayer of thanks that Sunny was with her. No one else had ever given her such strong unfailing support. And she needed every bit of it to get through what lay ahead of them.

CHAPTER ELEVEN

SUNNY drove at a hectic pace, with total disregard for tyres, condition of the road, any impediment whatsoever, and the Range Rover was up on top of the cliff face in less than fifteen minutes. Jackie endured Sunny's mad recklessness without a word, grateful for it in this race against time. It had started to rain, cold lashing sheets of it, and the thought of Robert being wet as well as cold was enough to chill her to the bone.

'Over there!' Edmund shouted, pointing to the ropes as they jumped out of the vehicle.

The wind was bitingly cold, the rain pouring down in drenching ferocity. Sunny didn't hesitate. He ran for the cliff edge. Jackie followed on his heels. Suddenly sensing her presence behind him, he turned and threw her back.

'Are you mad, woman?' he roared at her. 'Don't come any closer, it's too dangerous. This wind is enough to blow you off and I won't be responsible for your death. Now get back to safety at once. And keep Edmund away, too.'

Edmund . . . of course. God! She wasn't thinking sensibly at all. He was panting on her heels, not to be left out of any rescue attempt. She turned, snatched up his hand and hauled him back to a safe distance. They watched Sunny crawl to the cliff edge, heard him hollering downwards. The words were whipped away with the wind. He crawled back a few yards, then sprang to his feet and ran to the Range Rover. He opened up the back and dragged out a rope before Jackie could even reach him.

'What's happening?' she cried, plucking desperately at his arm. 'Is ... is Robert all right?'

He clutched her shoulder in a steadying manner, his eyes commanding her not to panic. 'He's a long way down. Over a hundred feet. I thought I heard him answer.'

She swallowed hard. 'What ... what are we going to do?' Already the sky was darkening ominously, the clouds obliterating the light.

'You and Edmund are to stand here. Shine the big spotlight torches so that the helicopter can see where we are when it comes. And anyone else who might be along to help.'

Then he was striding away from her, stopping at a sturdy iron-bark, tying the end of the rope around the tree. She ran after him, unable to control the panic that was clawing at her heart.

'What are you going to do?' The words came out on a near-hysterical sob, and the sobs kept shaking out of her.

Sunny threw her a hard glare. 'I'm going down to untangle the bloody ropes while there's still some light left. For God's sake, get a hold on yourself!'

She tried but the sobs couldn't be stopped. 'Can't ... can't we just ... pull Robert up?'

'Do you want him battered to death against the overhang?' he demanded fiercely.

'No ... no-o ...'

'Then we'll do it my way.' He began to tie the rope around his chest, under his shoulders.

Jackie reached out a trembling hand to touch him. 'Sunny ...' She managed to swallow down a sob, her eyes imploring his patience. 'Sunny, do you know what you're doing?'

He smiled his love at her. 'Of course I do.'

She sighed in grateful relief.

A boyish grin lit his face. 'I had a lot of practice at it when I was in Holland.'

He was off before she could say another word, paying out the rope, edging back towards the cliff. Then into her churning mind came the nerve-shattering realisation. As far as Jackie knew, there wasn't even a hill in Holland, let alone a real mountain.

In glazed shock she watched Sunny drop the rope over the edge, saw it tighten in his hand as he reached the cliff face, saw the grimly determined set of his facial muscles as he eased himself over the ledge. Then he was gone, into the gathering gloom, the howling wind and the sheets of rain.

Another realisation hit her with even more shocking force. Sunny wasn't abseiling, he didn't have two ropes, only the one. And he was going down that rope hand over hand. Over a hundred feet to the overhang, he had said. And then he would be holding on to his rope with one hand while he tried to unravel Robert's tangled ropes with the other. It was impossible. It couldn't be done. Sunny was bound to fall. And when he did the knotted rope around his chest would either break every rib in his body or squeeze him to death.

Jackie wrung her hands in grieving despair, forced to acknowledge her impotence to help. How could she have let Sunny go? He was bound to to be killed, even more certainly than Robert. Geoff had taught her enough about abseiling to know that Robert's only risk came from the elements. Sunny King was risking his life. For her son. And for her.

A hand tucked around her arm. 'Don't cry, Mum. It'll be all right now. Robert's strong. He can take anything. He won't be hurt.'

She looked down into Edmund's fear-filled eyes, so bravely trying to be brave, and she took him in her arms, hugging him with a fierce mother-love. 'I know that, darling. We'll get Robert back.' Please, God, she prayed, let them both be safe.

It grew darker, the rain a relentless downpour, the wind a howling dervish, gusting up the valley in whirling bursts. The conditions made any chance of survival a torturous nightmare. Jackie watched the rope, willing the thread of life to remain steady. If the rope went slack then Sunny would have fallen. She kept her fingers on it, feeling the tension and every slight movement. She found herself mumbling a litany. 'Please, God, keep it tight. Don't let him fall.'

Edmund tugged at her coat. 'Mum, we should have the torches on.'

'Of course. You're right, Edmund.'

'And we should put the headlights of the Range Rover on, Mum. They'll be a lot more powerful than the torches.'

Why hadn't she thought of that herself? She had to control her emotions, think clearly. Lives depended on it. 'Thank you Edmund. Yes. We should do that straight away.'

But it was hard to leave the rope. She had to force herself to follow the lead of her son. No sooner had she switched the headlights on than she heard the noise, the heavy beat of the rotor-blades from a far distance. It cleared her mind to razor-sharpness.

'Edmund, take the torches and place them at right angles in the clearing over there, so that the beams of light intersect at the middle of it.'

The very act of decision helped her to pull herself together. She had to keep control, do the right things, act in the way that would best help Sunny and Robert. She heard the helicopter drawing rapidly closer, going out over the cliff edge. A huge spotlight flashed on, illuminating what was happening below. She checked to see that Edmund had the torches aligned correctly. The helicopter hovered overhead, then slowly, ever so slowly, started to descend.

At last help was at hand. Relief flooded through Jackie. Hang on, Sunny, hang on, Robert, she silently chanted. We'll have you up in no time. She turned on a buoyant step and looked at the rope attached to the iron-bark, clearly outlined in the glow from the Range Rover's headlights.

It had gone completely slack!

Pain stabbed her heart. She sank to her knees, a cry of distress screaming straight from her soul. She closed her eyes, hugged her arms tightly around the piercing ache and keened for Sunny King, for the life of a man she had come to love, a man so opposite to her yet so inexpressibly dear, so . . .

'Cease that boo-hooing at once, Jackie. Is that any way to greet a man back? And there's still a bit of work to be done yet.'

For one stunned, disbelieving moment, Jackie stared uncomprehendingly at the face above her: Sunny's face, pale from fatigue, water dripping down it, but Sunny's face nevertheless.

'I've done it,' he told her proudly. 'The ropes are untangled; we can haul him up. And I've spoken to Robert. Nothing wrong with him.'

Jackie flew at him, hurling her arms around him, heart pounding a paean of joy and relief. 'Thank God you're safe! You're both safe!'

'Dirk Vescum looks after his own.' Sunny declared with grand smugness.

Jackie began to giggle. Hysterically. He was a child, nothing but a big, grown-up child. Or was he simply being facetious to relax her tension? She swallowed the mad giggle and raised hesitant eyes, probing the darkness of his eyes, trying to probe into the heart of him.

'What's going on here?' It was the bark of authority.

Sunny tucked Jackie under his arm and faced two burly men. 'Abseil the boy up. I'm pretty well beat,' he said on a telling sigh.

'No trouble,' one of the men said cheerfully.

'Hey, Mum! I came up under my own steam,' a chirpy voice informed her.

'Robert!' Jackie whirled out of Sunny's arms and gathered her wilful, wayward son into a crushing embrace.

'Hey! Go easy, Mum,' he protested.

'Are you hurt?' she asked anxiously, instantly loosening her hold.

'Nah! It was a breeze.'

'A breeze!' Jackie choked.

'Isn't there anything for us to do?' came the critical voice of authority. It sounded disappointed.

'Bit of a false alarm,' Sunny declared off-handedly.

'Well, we still have to take the boy to hospital.'

Jackie swung around to face the spokesman, her heart leaping in agitation at the idea of Robert having to go to hospital.

A genial face smiled at her and a beefy hand was thrust out. 'I'm Dr Meares. Mrs Mulholland, is it? Mother of the boy?'

She weakly grasped his hand and nodded.

'It's just for observation. One night in hospital won't hurt him. No need for alarm. Rules and regulations, you know. He looks perfectly all right to me but we must follow form.'

'But . . .'

'Now don't worry, dear.' The doctor patted her hand. 'There's no need for you to come. We'll just take the boy along with us and pop him in for the night.'

'But is it necessary?' Jackie demanded anxiously.

The doctor shook his head. 'Not necessary. Not necessary at all. But we've got to do it. Rules and regulations in these rescue cases.' His face suddenly broke into a ribald grin. 'We had one case where we were called in. Woman had apparently died while having sex—only passed out really. By the time we got there she had quite recovered. Had to pull the husband off her. But we got her to hospital for observation. Rules and regulations. Can't go against them.'

'You've never passed out on me,' Sunny growled in Jackie's ear.

She ignored him, although a silly smile was tugging at her mouth. 'But, Doctor ...' she said firmly.

'Aw, Mum! Don't spoil it,' Robert pleaded. 'I've never been in a helicopter.'

'Robert, don't you interrupt your mother,' Sunny said sternly. 'You've done quite enough interrupting for one afternoon.'

'Yessir,' Robert mumbled humbly.

'It's only for twenty-four hours, Mrs Mulholland,' the doctor explained. 'You can come and collect him tomorrow. If you want to,' he added with an arch look at Robert.

Jackie gave in. The doctor took hold of Robert and marched him over to the helicopter. Edmund mumbled something about Robert always having all the luck, which earned a sharp reprimand from

Sunny and a short lecture on the worry they had both given their mother. They stood in the rain and watched the safe departure of rules and regulations.

Sunny's arm curled around Jackie's shoulders, holding her with him as he spoke sternly to her younger son. 'Edmund, into the car!'

'Yessir,' he answered meekly, and scooted.

'Now, Jackie . . .'

His hand slid away. He walked about in considerable agitation, smacking his hands together as if beating up determined purpose. The rain was pouring down on both of them, but Jackie didn't think of suggesting that they should also return to the car. Her attention was entirely focused on this extraordinary man that she loved.

He shook an emphatic finger at her. 'Those boys of yours need discipline.' Spoken in the manner of a proclamation.

'Yes, I can see that,' she said demurely.

'Things cannot be permitted to go on the way they've been going.'

'You're right.'

'Those boys need a father. They desperately need a father.'

'It would be good for them.'

He stepped up and measured her, eyeball to eyeball. 'If they don't get a father soon, they'll be dead. And so will you. They need someone they admire and respect to take control, to . . .' He floundered for words.

'To rule them with a rod of iron,' Jackie supplied helpfully, her heart soaring with love for him.

Surprise flickered over his face. 'You agree with me?'

'Absolutely.'

'I can do it, Jackie. I'd be good for them. Once I was at the helm, they wouldn't step out of line. They need someone like me. Control and discipline. It's for your own good, Jackie. And theirs.' He was almost pleading.

She smiled all her love at him. 'Sunny, there is no one in the whole world like you.'

He frowned suspiciously at her. 'Do you really mean that?'

She remembered all she had thought and felt while he had been down on the cliff face. 'I know it,' she said fervently.

His eyes searched hers anxiously. 'I wouldn't let you go, you know. Lifetime job. Total commitment. Nothing less would satisfy.

She looked up at him dreamily. 'You are a beautiful, beautiful man, Sunny King.'

'Living with me all the time ... you might not like that,' he continued, almost as if he hadn't heard her, or couldn't quite believe her. 'I know I'm not perfect. Though I wouldn't say that to anyone else. But you'd have to be happy with me, Jackie. Your needs, your wants, are more important to me than my own.'

'I'd do anything for you, Sunny. Anything at all.'

'When will you marry me?' he instantly demanded.

'As soon as you like,' she sighed blissfully.

He wrapped her in an iron-tight embrace and poured kisses all over her head. 'You're getting wet, Jackie,' he sighed. 'I think it's raining. We'd better go home.'

'Yes. Home,' she agreed even more blissfully.

He bundled her into the Range Rover, wrapped a blanket around her, then took the driver's seat. In a totally uncharacteristic move, he drove home at a sedate, safety-conscious pace, a smile never leaving his lips and one hand firmly enfolding one of Jackie's.

It seemed that all the lights in the house were on. The garage door was open. Betty and Tom Willis were standing there with Trevor, waiting to do anything that was required. Their welcoming smiles said they already knew that Robert had been safely rescued. As soon as the Range Rover pulled to a halt, Trevor had the back door open and Edmund hoisted into his arms.

'You little monkey,' he said affectionately. 'Don't you ever do that without me again.'

'Get him into a bath, Trevor,' Sunny ordered as he swiftly alighted. 'Betty, look after him, will you? Feed him and put him to bed?'

'Of course I will,' the housekeeper agreed, already fussing over Edmund.

Jackie was still trying to untangle herself from the blanket when Sunny opened her door and swept her up into his arms. 'I'm all right. I can walk,' she protested feebly.

'I'm going to put you in the sauna. Stop you getting a cold. Most important,' Sunny muttered, cradling her even closer to him.

'Need my help, Sunny?' Tom Willis asked.

'No thanks, Tom. This case needs my care. My particular loving care,' he murmured, brushing his warm mouth across Jackie's forehead.

She had no inclination whatsoever to protest against that. As far as she was concerned, Sunny was the boss. And always would be. She could not be in better hands, hands that she knew would protect her, support her, love her; and what more could she possibly want? He was a man amongst men, Sunny King. The very best.

CHAPTER TWELVE

EDMUND begged to accompany them on the drive to pick up Robert from Royal Prince Alfred Hospital in Sydney. He had never been inside a big hospital and he didn't see why Robert should always have all the advantages. Although, of course, he was also concerned about seeing for himself that Robert was all right.

Sunny laughingly agreed that Edmund should come with them. His good humour was so expansive this morning that Jackie privately thought he would agree to anything. However, she herself was somewhat troubled. While she had no doubts about her feelings for Sunny—the acute sense of loss she had experienced last night left no room for doubt at all on that issue—her commitment to him did pose some practical problems.

For one thing, she couldn't be sure how the boys would react to the news. While they admired and liked Sunny, she also knew they revered the memory of their father. She decided that she would sound them out gradually on the idea of remarriage.

The other factor that worried her was the lack of common interests between herself and Sunny. From her experience of being married to Geoff, Jackie knew how important it was for a married couple to be able to share and talk about things together. Without those common bonds to link them it was all too easy for people to drift apart, no matter how much they loved one another.

She pondered on these problems while Sunny drove them into the city in the Diamler. To Edmund's disgust and Jackie's relief, the whole trip was negotiated at a very conservative speed. When they arrived at the hospital they found Robert chatting up the patients and staff. As Dr Meares had assured Jackie the night before, her irresponsible son had suffered no harm at all from his perilous escapade, but she said quite a few wounding words to him on the way home to make up for it.

A couple of days slipped by and Jackie threw out several leading comments to the boys, but she hadn't actually declared her intention to marry Sunny when he himself raised the issue and a few other matters. It was late at night and they were lying on their bed in the warm afterglow of satisfaction given and received.

'Have you spoken to the boys yet?' he suddenly asked.

Jackie sighed, feeling a little bit guilty about her hesitancy. She didn't want Sunny to feel slighted in any way. 'I've been hinting at it but I haven't actually told them yet. I think I'll do it tomorrow,' she said cautiously.

She might just as well have saved herself the bit of heartburn. 'There won't be any trouble there,' he said with his usual arrogant confidence.

A niggle of exasperation crept into her voice. 'How can you be so sure?'

'They think I'm wonderful,' he said modestly.

A giggle tickled her throat but she swallowed it down with a smile. 'So do I, but I'm not certain that will be enough for them.'

'You'll see,' Sunny said confidently. 'However, there is one problem we do have to resolve.'

'What's that?' Jackie asked, feeling alarmed that Sunny also saw a problem for them.

'This house.'

'What's wrong with it?'

'You don't like it.'

'I do, I do, I do,' Jackie sang in sheer relief that the problem was not a problem at all.

'You said you didn't. You said ...'

'I've changed my mind,' she insisted.

He looked at her suspiciously. 'For a clever woman, you change your mind a lot.'

'That's because of you.'

'What do I do?'

She grinned her love at him. 'You strike at the heart. And that changes any woman's perception of things.'

For a moment he grinned back in pleasure, but a frown quickly gathered again. 'Are you sure? If you want to redecorate ...'

'The only thing I'd change ...' Jackie commenced firmly.

'Yes?'

'... are those rotten statues.'

'I'll get Tom Willis to take them to the dump tomorrow. What will you put in their place?'

'Wait and see.' She smiled her contentment. Somehow Sunny's compulsive need to see to her happiness put her mind at rest. Her eyes caressed him with a deep gratitude that he was her man. 'Why have you never married, Sunny?' she asked, thinking how terribly lucky she was that he hadn't.

He thought for a minute, then replied, 'There were two reasons. Most of my life I lived in abject poverty and I'd never subject a woman I loved to that.'

'And the second?'

He rolled on to his side and looked down at her, smiling as he stroked her cheek with featherlight tenderness. 'I'd never met anyone I truly admired until I met you. Certainly no one I ever loved.'

And Jackie's contentment stretched to an even deeper level. In fact, she felt so good that, when morning came, it didn't take too much courage at all to broach the boys with the announcement that she and Sunny were getting married. However, their reaction immediately dimmed her happiness.

'No, Mum! You're not!' Robert said in shocked tones. 'You can't!'

'We don't believe it!' Edmund joined in with even more shock. 'Don't do it, Mum!'

Tears welled into Jackie's eyes.

'Aw, gee, Mum! Don't get upset,' Robert begged in an instant *volte-face*. 'We were only joking. Truly we were. We knew you were going to marry Sunny, and we thought it would be fun to pull your leg a bit.'

'Yeah. We knew ever since we saw you kissing Sunny in his bedroom that night we came up to watch the party,' Edmund informed her smugly.

Robert looked equally smug as he added, 'It was

obvious that it was only a matter of time, Mum, so we decided ...'

'You don't really mind?' Jackie asked dazedly.

They answered in enthusiastic tandem, 'No, we think it's great ...'

'Having a Dad at long last ...'

'Should have done it years ago, Mum ...'

'Months ago, anyway. When Sunny first asked you ...'

'We wouldn't have had to do all that painting ...'

'Yeah. Best thing we ever did was burn down the house ...'

'Though we didn't mean it at the time, Mum ...'

Jackie just shook her head and wandered away, too relieved to bother taking them to task about anything. Besides, Sunny had said he would do that from now on, and, God knew, he would learn soon enough how big a responsibility he had shouldered.

Having received her sons' blessing, Jackie confidently went ahead with the wedding arrangements. Sunny was no help. When she asked him where he wanted to go for their honeymoon, his eyes went all dreamy and he replied, 'It doesn't matter. Wherever you like. I'd be happy anywhere with you.'

Jackie decided that Surfers' Paradise on the Queensland Gold Coast was probably the best place. It was only a thousand kilometres away and it wouldn't be too dreadfully expensive. She was finalising the arrangements when Sunny wandered into the room that had been allotted as her study, a look of absolute bliss on his face.

'I've found it, Jackie, and I've done it!'

A now-familiar tingle of apprehension crept down her spine. 'What have you found and what have you done?' she asked warily.

'I've chartered a sailing boat. Big. Really big. A hundred and twenty feet long. Fully crewed. We'll cruise around the Pacific islands then down the South American coast for our honeymoon. We'll be waited on hand and foot. Not a stroke of work has to be done. Just stay with each other and enjoy the balmy days and nights ...'

Jackie looked at the booking arrangements on her desk, carefully screwed up the forms and dropped them in the wastepaper basket. She stood up and slipped into his enthusiastic embrace. 'I couldn't think of anything more perfect,' she agreed.

He beamed down at her. 'You're the most sensible woman I've ever met.'

Someone had to be sensible in this crazy house, she thought ruefully, but when the madness was divine, it was much easier to be swept along with it. Although she found herself shaking her head a lot, like over the issue of her dieting. Jackie thought she would look better if she lost a few pounds but Sunny instantly put a halt to that.

'You're not to deprive me of any bit of you,' he declared.

Which was fine by her. If Sunny liked her exactly as she was, so much the better. And really she didn't look too bad. But then he went on to declare, 'Jackie, for the rest of your life, you're only to do what you want to do.'

That was a bit much, coming on top of his order to stop dieting, but she suppressed a tart comment because she knew he was speaking from the heart.

Jackie made a major discovery in the weeks that led up to their wedding. It wasn't sharing things that made a relationship work. It was giving your partner what they needed. Sunny was such a compulsive giver to her that Jackie was in no doubt about his love, and she found that the more she adopted his approach and gave to him, the greater her love for him became.

By the time their wedding day arrived, she had come to the realisation that there was nothing she would not do to make him happy and contented. Sunny had taught her so much about loving that she felt very humble indeed, recognising at last just how much she had missed out on life.

They were married in the little historic church at St Alban's, thus presenting respectability in its most traditional form to all the local inhabitants, and erasing any possible blot on Jackie's reputation. The popular opinion was that it was a good thing, since Jackie Mulholland was a straight, level-headed woman who deserved a decent kind of man.

The honeymoon was all Sunny had promised it would be and they came home on a blissful wave of contentment. Trevor met them in the Daimler and transported them back to St Alban's. Robert and Edmund were at the front door to greet them, their faces lit with joyous welcome.

'It's grand to have you back, Mum,' Robert piped at her. 'And you, too, Dad.'

'Yeah. Dad. We love you, too,' Edmund added in

a burst of feeling.

Jackie beamed at them proudly. They hadn't had any prompting. Their acceptance of Sunny as their dad, their loving welcome ... they were behaving just as she had always wished they would behave. Her heart swelled with happiness. Sunny had said they needed a father and the improvement in their conduct was evident already.

Sunny clapped them on the shoulder. 'Good to be back, boys.'

'Ah, Dad ...'

'Yes, Robert?'

'While Trevor was ... er ... picking you and Mum up ...'

'Yes?'

'I was teaching Edmund how to drive ... the Lagonda ...'

'And this tree ran into the road,' Edmund put in appealingly.

'And crashed straight into the radiator,' Robert finished quickly.

Jackie felt herself go faint.

A bull-like roar issued from her new husband. 'That's it!' He glowered with rage. 'That's the end! Solitary confinement! Neither of you are to see a movie, watch television, go anywhere, do anything, for a whole week. And if you disobey me I'll whip your bottoms so hard you'll never walk again.' His voice rose several decibels. 'Nor drive a car!'

He swept a commanding arm towards the staircase. 'Go! You are banished to your rooms. The death penalty for disobedience. I don't want to see your faces again for seven days. Except for coming and going to school,' he amended grudgingly. 'Do you understand me, gentlemen?'

'Yes, Dad,' two tiny voices chorused. They turned and fled before the wrath of their new father.

Jackie turned apprehensively to her enraged husband and slid appeasing hands over his hard, inflated chest. 'I'm so sorry, Sunny. I never dreamed that they . . .' She faltered to a stop as he suddenly grinned at the retreating backs of two frightened little boys.

Then he looked down at her and began to chuckle. 'Those little monsters are going to get sorted out. Before I'm finished with them they'll be human.' He curved an arm around Jackie's shoulders and winked at her. 'Actually, I've got a terrible confession to make.'

'What is it?' she asked, feeling light-hearted again.

'When I was their age I did the same thing to my dad's car.'

'Oh, Sunny!' she laughed. 'And what did he do to you?'

'The same as they got.'

'Well, you did say that Robert and Edmund needed a father,' she reminded him with a teasing smile.

He growled into his beard. 'They've got that all right.' He started walking her towards the staircase which led to their room. 'Now, Jackie, for their own good, we've got to get started straight away,' he said in his voice of authority.

She looked up at him, completely nonplussed. 'I don't understand. Start what?'

'What our sons need are sisters. Give them a sense of responsibility. Looking after others. It's the only sensible thing to do.' The no-nonsense tone dropped to one of anticipated pleasure. 'A baby girl. I'd be very good with a girl, Jackie.'

'I know you would, Sunny.' Her voice caressed him with her pleasure.

And she was only thirty-one. Young enough to have several girls, if they were blessed with daughters. If they had sons, then Sunny would be to blame, because men determined the sex of any child. Would she tell him? No, not yet. Only if the baby turned out to be a boy. And maybe not even then.

She looked up at him. Sunny would be wonderful with babies. She was sure of that. Sometimes she thought he was still a baby himself, but when they reached the bedroom, she was strongly reminded that he was definitely a very grown-up, very virile and loving man.

Some considerable time later they lay contentedly in each other's arms. Alena's dramatic line in the last Dirk Vescum movie ran through Jackie's mind ... 'Do you think I would want to live without you?' That was precisely how she felt about Sunny. She hugged him more tightly, knowing how precious this man was to her continued happiness. Her love for him tingled through her brain, through her whole body.

Suddenly he propped himself up to look down at her. 'I've decided ... and I won't take no for an answer, Jackie ... that you're to be the musical director for all my movies.'

'But I ... I really don't have the expertise, Sunny.'

'Course you do. You can do anything. Same as myself. In fact, what I'm going to do is make a movie about our relationship. The world is starving for a love-story like ours.'

'But, Sunny ...'

'Hush, woman.' He silenced her with a kiss that was worth being silenced for. When he lifted his head a beatific smile was spreading over his face. 'I have this vision ...'

And who was she to question a vision, Jackie thought, and happily settled herself to listen to the beautifully mad, hopelessly egocentric man that she loved.

THE POSITIVE APPROACH

Claim your FREE books and gifts here

Yes Please send me three books and two gifts absolutely FREE. Please also reserve a special Reader Service subscription for me. If I decide to subscribe, I will receive two each of the very latest titles from the Mills & Boon Romance, Medical Romance and Silhouette Sensation series every month. Six books for just £10.10 postage and packing FREE, thats less than £1.70 per book. If I decide not to subscribe I shall write to you within 10 days. The FREE books and gifts remain mine to keep in any case. I understand that I am under no obligation whatsoever. I may cancel or suspend my subscription at any time simply by writing to you. I am over 18 years of age.

8A2X

Ms/Mrs/Miss/Mr —————————————————

Address —————————————————

—————————————————

————————— Postcode —————————

Signature —————————————————

Reader Service
FREEPOST
P.O. Box 236
Croydon
Surrey CR9 9EL

Send NO money now

THE POSITIVE APPROACH

BY
EMMA DARCY

MILLS & BOON LIMITED
Eton House, 18-24 Paradise Road
Richmond, Surrey TW9 1SR

First published in Great Britain in 1987
by Mills & Boon Limited

© Emma Darcy 1987

Australian copyright 1987
Philippine copyright 1987
Reprinted 1987
This edition 1992

ISBN 0 263 77940 8

Set in Plantin 11 on 13 pt.
19-9208-39218

Made and printed in Great Britain

For Karen,
who wants to know if it really works out.

CHAPTER ONE

TWELVE pairs of eyes bored into Sarah.

For the last ten minutes she had welcomed their focused attention, but the interest she had generated around the conference table with her proposal had now turned to irritation. She herself was appalled at the interruption. She could hardly believe it. To be asked to take a personal telephone call . . . and in the middle of her sales pitch! It was unbelievable. No one—not for any reason—interrupted a conference. They were sacrosanct.

The secretary's eyes were full of apologetic appeal. Her hands were fumbling together in agitation. She knew how bad the situation was, and she also knew that she would probably have to bear the brunt of the blame for such an unprecedented move. Her voice shook as she stood her ground and reinforced her message.

'Your fiancé said it was extremely urgent and important, Miss Woodley. He would not take no for an answer and was most emphatic that it couldn't wait.'

The poor girl was distraught and it was obvious that Julian had wrung this action out of her. What could be so urgent and important? Sarah wondered dazedly, then pulled her wits together. It was paramount that she make a quick decision. Everyone was looking at her ., . . waiting . . . and every moment lost would be counted against her. Besides, she had no choice. If it really was urgent and important she had to go to Julian.

Sarah knew exactly how the secretary felt. Blood was pounding through her head as she forced herself to meet the eyes around the table. She could see the judgement in them. At twenty-eight she was the youngest departmental manager in the room, and that in itself was a ready-to-hand indictment for breaking a rule that the older managers had always respected.

'Please excuse me. I won't be long,' she said as steadily as she could, but even she could hear the tremulous note in her voice.

The chairman nodded. That was all. Nobody said a word. Conscious of the thick silence behind her, Sarah made as fast an exit as could be made with dignity. The secretary followed on her heels, babbling directions to the telephone holding the open line to Julian. Sarah snatched up the receiver, every nerve jangling with alarm as she spoke.

'What's the matter, Julian?'

'Sarah . . .' It was a sigh of exasperation. 'What took you so long?'

Her inner tension drove a sharp edge to her voice. 'I'm not supposed to be here, Julian. I'm still in conference.'

He laughed. A totally uncaring laugh. A red haze spread through Sarah's brain. Only the most rigid self-discipline held it at bay. 'You said it was urgent and important, Julian,' she reminded him tightly.

He took an infuriating length of time getting to the point. Sarah listened with a weird sense of unreality. He had called her out of conference to ask if he'd left some documents in her apartment the previous night. He didn't need them right now. He simply wanted to feel reassured that they had not been misplaced elsewhere. The matter was not so urgent or important that it could not have waited. Another hour or two would have made no difference at all.

Sarah felt too sick to argue the point with him. He had probably set her career back years, just on a selfish whim. She gave him his reassurance in a dead, flat voice and hung up on him. She stared blankly at the secretary for a long, frozen moment. The girl's hands fluttered apologetically.

'He said he wouldn't let you work here any more if I didn't get you.'

The red haze gathered volcanic force, blotting out any compassion for the girl's dilemma. 'No more calls,' Sarah commanded harshly. 'Not for any reason. Now or in the future. I don't care what anyone says. No more calls.'

'Yes, Miss Woodley,' came the quivering reply.

But the damage was done. Sarah knew it as soon as she re-entered the conference room. No one looked at her except the chairman who informed her very briefly that they had considered her proposal for a new fashion line and decided that it carried too high a risk factor. Better to stick to proven lines where the profitability was certain.

Sarah flicked a look at Frances Chatfield, the manager of the Ladies' Fashion department. The triumph in the older woman's eyes told her that Frances had swung her entrenched influence against the proposal. Sarah had expected it. Frances Chatfield fiercely resented that Young Trends had been made into a separate department and given into the charge of a younger woman. Julian's call had delivered the perfect opportunity for her to suggest that Sarah's judgement was unreliable. The suggestion had taken root well and truly. Sarah could see it written all over their faces. In huge letters. UNRELIABLE.

Normally she fought for what she believed in. But to do that now with any chance of success she had to be calm and rational. The boiling rage inside her made such a state of mind impossible. If she spoke, she would only compound the damage. To all outward appearances she accepted defeat gracefully and was an attentive, respectful listener for the rest of the meeting.

The next seven hours were a different matter. She seethed over Julian's arrogant presumption that his needs had total priority over everything else. Never mind *her* career! Her job wasn't important enough for him to give it any serious consideration at all. He didn't care that his damned telephone call had undermined every bit of respect she had ever fought for.

Sarah prided herself on being tolerant. Dealing with customers in her Young Trends department made tolerance absolutely necessary, and the occasional necessity of dealing with Frances Chatfield demanded even more—tactful diplomacy and the patience of a saint. But by the time five o'clock came round, Sarah didn't feel at all tolerant. Her temper was sizzling on a very short fuse.

With a thoroughly jaundiced eye she scanned the oncoming stream of peak-hour traffic as she stood on the pavement outside the department store, waiting for Julian. When she spotted the red Alfa Romeo she moved to the kerb on a surge of angry impatience and ignored Julian's smile as he pulled in to pick her up. She slid quickly into the passenger seat and the short rein on her temper was frayed even further by his heavy-footed burst of acceleration. How many times had she told him she didn't like being jerked backwards while she was trying to fasten the seat-belt?

'It's great to have the week's work finished,' he tossed at her brightly. 'Did you have a good day?'

'No, thanks to you,' grated Sarah. 'And it may have escaped your notice, Julian, but my weekend doesn't start on Friday afternoon. I do have to work Saturday mornings as well.'

He frowned. 'We'll have to do something about that when we're married, Sarah. This working on Saturdays will interfere with our weekends together. Maybe you should start looking for a less demanding job.'

The last thread of control snapped. Sarah glared her fury and frustration at the man beside her. Neither the handsome profile nor the smart executive image that Julian affected so well made any softening impression on her. The words spilled off her tongue with all the steam of a pressure cooker whose lid had been lifted.

'Nothing can interfere with your plans, can it, Julian?' she stormed at him. 'In case it hasn't penetrated yet, let me tell you again. I *like* my job. I do not appreciate your cavalier attitude towards it. I particularly do not appreciate being pulled out of an important conference for an unnecessary telephone call. You know that such calls are completely against the company policy.'

He shot her a needled look. 'Now, hold on a minute, Sarah. That call was important. I was worried about those papers.'

'You could have waited an hour. You could have waited all day. If you had been the slightest bit thoughtful, you could have left a message for me to ring you back,' she retorted heatedly.

He laughed that same uncaring laugh. And then he patted her knee as he spoke with amused indulgence. 'Darling, it was in your own interests.

It was a way of showing those petty women you work with that when you're with me, their little power games don't matter. Now, what difference did it make?'

'They wouldn't listen to me, that's what difference it made, Julian,' she fired at him furiously. 'They'll probably never listen to my ideas again. And we're going to lose out on a contract with one of the most exciting young designers on the fashion scene, because Frances Chatfield hasn't got the eye to see it, and they no longer trust me to judge what's profitable or not.'

Julian shrugged. 'Well, why should you? You won't even need a job after we're married. I don't see what you're making so much fuss about,' he argued dismissively.

And he never would see, Sarah decided on a wave of disgust—disgust with his male chauvinist ego, and disgust at the way she had kept swallowing it all up until now. She hadn't minded Julian's arrogance at first. She had always admired ambitious, strong-minded men who knew where they were going and knew what they wanted out of life. But she did have a few ideas and plans of her own, and ever since she had accepted Julian's proposal of marriage, he had started to disregard them. From the moment she had said yes, it seemed that her feelings didn't count any more.

This wasn't the first argument they had had on the matter, but it was going to be the last, Sarah silently determined. She was not going to live the rest of her life with a man who always put himself first. If he treated his fiancée as a second-class citizen, how was he going to treat his wife? Particularly a wife who gave up all independence to have his children? Sarah was not so blinded by her emotional attachment to Julian that she couldn't see the kind of future that was staring her in the face, and she couldn't ignore it any longer.

'Oh, by the way, I ran into an old acquaintance today,' Julian remarked, completely unaware of her burning anger. He threw her a condescending smile. 'He's only in Sydney this weekend, so I promised I'd have lunch with him tomorrow. It'll make us a bit late leaving for your parents' place, but an hour or two won't matter.'

Sarah's anger gathered furnace heat. 'Funnily enough, it does matter, Julian.'

He sliced her a look that said she was being petty. 'If good humour is to be maintained, my sweet, the shorter the time we have with your parents, the better.'

'Let's make that no time at all,' she bit out decisively.

He sighed. 'Don't be unreasonable, Sarah. I'll put myself out to please your parents, but ...'

'Don't bother. There's no reason for you to put yourself out for me or my parents. We're finished, Julian. This is the end.' She pulled off her ring and very deliberately placed it on the dashboard.

And finally he did take some notice of her. His smug composure broke into angry exasperation. 'For God's sake! Not another tantrum about your parents. You've said yourself that the only conversation they have is about gardening and lawn-bowls and bridge. It'll be a damned bore to me, but I'm willing ...'

'Forget it!' Sarah sliced in even more angrily. 'You're as free as a bird.'

'Don't be silly,' he said with a return to pompous arrogance.

'I'm not,' retorted Sarah emphatically.

He heaved a very patient sigh. 'You are being ridiculous. This is a foolish, self-defeating decision of yours, Sarah. It's not as if you're a young, skittish girl with lots of marriage prospects in front of you. The thing I've always appreciated about you is how sensible and reasonable you are ...'

Sarah seethed in stony silence, scorning any reply to his self-serving arguments. He pulled up at her apartment block in Neutral Bay with the usual abrupt braking that jerked her forward. She slammed out of the car. Julian followed her at a run. With absolute disdain for his heated expostulations, she marched straight into an open elevator and pressed the button for her floor. Julian accompanied her up, his face becoming quite red as she maintained her silence.

He grabbed her arm as she stepped out of the elevator, but Sarah tore it from his grasp and made a pointed business of getting her key out of her handbag. She noticed with an almost curious detachment that Julian's frustration was making him look quite ugly. The suave, man-about-town veneer was crumbling.

She unlocked her door and swept inside the apartment she shared with her friend, Angela Haviland. She hoped Angela was at home. Her presence would surely stem Julian's protests.

A rustle of newspaper drew her gaze to the couch. A big man lay stretched out on it, feet dangling over the end and head propped up on a cushion for easy reading. Sarah's step faltered for a moment. Who the devil was he? One of Angela's boyfriends? He had to be a new acquisition, because Sarah had never seen him before in her life.

She gave herself a quick mental shrug. Whoever he was he meant nothing to her. Her first priority was to get Julian off her back and out of her life. She swooped on the folder of notes that had been left on the coffee table last night and wheeled on Julian, who had spluttered into silence at the sight of the stranger.

'Here are your precious notes! They're more important to you than I am, so take them and go!' She thrust them into his hands.

There was a rustle of newspaper and Julian flicked a resentful glance at the man behind her. 'We have to talk about this, Sarah,' he said in a low, threatening tone.

'There's nothing more to say. I'm not cut out to suit your convenience, Julian. Go find yourself another doormat, because I'm not going to be one for you any more. I'd rather stay on the shelf by myself than live with you on your terms.'

'Now, Sarah . . .' he tossed the folder on to the nearest armchair and took a firm hold of her upper arms, ' . . . you can't change your mind like this. And when I say we'll talk, that means we're going to talk.'

'Let go of me, Julian,' she hissed, her inner rage boiling up again at his domineering tactics.

He ignored her, his gaze stabbing over her shoulder to the man on the couch. 'Would you mind leaving us alone? This is private.'

'Oh, no, you don't!' Sarah snapped, and out of sheer frustration that he wouldn't take notice of her, she drew back her foot and kicked him as hard as she could on the shin.

Julian flung her away with an angry oath. Thrown off balance, Sarah crashed back into the coffee table, stumbled over and felt herself falling backwards. She landed on the floor with a resounding thump along with the upturned table, a cup and saucer, and the frog ornament of which Angela was so fond. Her stunned gaze caught a blur of movement.

'Steady on, old chap. We can't be hitting women now, can we?'

The voice was modulated with sweet good

humour but, as Sarah's vision cleared, she saw that the stranger had Julian's wrist in a vice-like grip, and despite the tone of sweet reason, there was something definitely threatening about his stance next to her erstwhile fiancé. He was a very big man, taller and broader than Julian, and the track suit he wore fairly bulged with well developed muscles.

'Who are you?' demanded Julian, forced to take the stranger into consideration and furious with his interference.

The stranger ignored him, looking down at Sarah with a troubled frown. 'Are you hurt?' he asked, his voice softening to real concern.

'I ... I don't think so,' she said, testing her shaken limbs as she dragged herself into a sitting position.

'What do you want me to do with him—throw him out the window or the door?'

He could do it too, Sarah thought on a hysterical note of whimsy, and obviously Julian thought the same. 'I'll leave under my own steam,' he blustered, trying to pull his arm out of the stranger's grasp, but to no avail. He glared balefully at Sarah. 'It's obvious you've been two-timing me on the side. It's got nothing to do with your damned parents, has it?'

'I think the window. It's the least troublesome thing to do,' the big man said quietly, looking Julian straight in the eye.

'We're four storeys up,' gasped Sarah.

'A good dropping height,' he agreed. 'Gives him a nice view on the way down.'

Fear instantly shrivelled Julian's bravado. 'You're a maniac!' he squawked.

'Some very thick-headed people have called me that from time to time,' his captor conceded pleasantly.

'Let him go,' Sarah sighed, weary of the distasteful scene.

The big man leaned over, picked up the folder of the notes and presented it to Julian with a smile so benevolent that it spelled the most terrible danger. 'I'd go while the going was still easy if I were you,' he said softly.

Julian almost scuttled away, only pausing to square his shoulders into some dignity as he reached the door. 'You haven't heard the last of this!' he snarled at Sarah.

The big man moved fractionally. Julian did not stop to hurl any more invective. He swung on his heel and was off, slamming the door behind him.

Sarah dragged in a deep breath. She suddenly felt quite sick and very shaky. Before she could bring herself to move, the stranger was kneeling beside her, tenderly brushing away the long bang of hair that had flopped across her cheek.

'Are you all right?'

It was the soft, caring tone that did it. Throughout this whole terrible day, no one had cared how she felt. Tears welled into her eyes. 'I . . . I'm not sure,' she choked out.

'Hey . . .' his smile was softly admiring, 'you can't fall apart on me now. The way you told that guy where to get off was terrific. Greatest speech I've ever heard from a woman. Real backbone.' And so saying, he slid his arms under Sarah and, seemingly without any effort at all, cradled her against him like a helpless baby as he pulled himself to his feet.

But Sarah was a long way from being a baby. Although she was slim, she was above average height and her figure was very much that of a woman. No man had ever swept her up in his arms like this and it gave her a funny, weak feeling to be enveloped by so much virile strength.

She found her head disconcertingly close to his. Rather dazedly she looked into a pair of vivid blue eyes that were sparkling with pleasure at her. His smile was vivid too. Very white in his tanned face. And he had dimples in his cheeks. Dimples that looked hopelessly incongruous in what was a rugged kind of face; a firm, squarish jawline, a strong, slightly bent nose, a small, pale scar cutting through one of his straight eyebrows, and thick, bristly brown hair that was cut in a short, neat style.

'Who are you?' she finally croaked, suddenly feeling that it was time she grasped some control over the situation. 'And what are you doing in my apartment?' she added, realising belatedly that Angela had not put in an appearance to claim him.

One eyebrow rose in amusement. 'You took the words right out of my mouth.'

Sarah didn't understand him. 'What do you mean?'

He grinned. 'I was about to ask the same thing. Not that I object, mind you. You're very welcome. But I would like to know who you are, and what you're doing in my apartment.'

Sarah's head whirled. If she wasn't mad, then she was in the clutches of a crazy intruder. 'I think you'd better put me down,' she said warily.

He considered it for a moment and then shook his head. 'You're better off where you are,' he said in a very decided tone.

She had no hope of fighting him, not from this helpless position. She had seen him hold Julian with one hand. She swallowed hard and tried to keep calm. 'I don't know what game you're playing, but I'm Sarah Woodley. And my flatmate, Angela Haviland, will be home any minute now.' If he had any designs on her, the thought of witnesses suddenly appearing might slow him down.

'Sarah,' he said, then gave a deep chuckle of satisfaction. 'So you're Angela's flatmate! But that's marvellous! Absolutely perfect. Couldn't be better if I'd put in a custom-made order.'

'What couldn't be better?' she demanded testily.

'Just let me think for a minute,' he commanded, and without any regard for her dignity at all, he paced around the room, still carrying her effortlessly as though she were a rag doll he had momentarily forgotten.

His face was such a deep study of concentration that Sarah wasn't sure if it was wise to break his train of thought. She was in a perilous position and she didn't want him throwing her out of the window. But he had mentioned Angela's name. That was a consoling thought. Except that she had mentioned it first, so that particular consolation wasn't very dependable.

He came to an abrupt halt and the blue eyes were suddenly stabbing straight into hers with decisive purpose. 'You'll do, Sarah. Under the circumstances, I couldn't possibly do better. No doubt about it. All the other women I know will only give me trouble. Every one of them. Angela is out scouting for me now, but that's grasping at straws.'

'What are you talking about?' Sarah shrilled, desperate to find some grain of sense in what he was saying.

He smiled. Under normal conditions it was a smile that would have inspired confidence in him, and for a moment, Sarah was dazzled into being a compliant listener again.

'Sarah, I've been looking for someone like you. Desperately. And now that we've got rid of your fiancé . . . and from what I saw of him, I'd say good riddance . . . we'll spend the whole weekend together, getting to know each other. Make sure it's right,' he added with relish.

Her compliance took an immediate dive. 'I am not going to spend the weekend with you,' she cried in panicky protest. 'Angela ...'

' ... is my sister. I bought this apartment for her and that's one of the reasons she'll do anything for me. I'm Ben Haviland, her older brother. And I'm delighted to meet you, Sarah Woodley. In fact, I wish I'd come home a lot sooner. It would have taken some of the worry off my mind. Only got in from the States yesterday. Slept off the jet lag in the Hilton Airport Hotel and contacted Angela first thing this morning. Speed is of the essence and I hate staying in hotels anyway. Never feel comfortable in them.'

The panic receded. Angela had often talked of her 'maverick' brother, Ben. With admiration and exasperation. But all the same, Sarah still could not feel comfortable with the situation. 'Please ... I think you should put me down.'

The eyebrows slanted an appeal. 'It feels good, holding you like this. And it's making you feel better. Tears all gone. Voice stronger. Colour in your cheeks ...'

'Please ... I would like to sit down,' Sarah insisted, aware of an even greater rush of colour to her cheeks. 'And where is Angela?'

'As I said, she's out scouting prospects for me,' he said patiently. 'She said she'd call you at work and let you know what was going on.'

Sarah remembered her order about no calls and

heaved a sigh. 'She couldn't get through to me. Not today.'

'Then that answers everything.'

It answered nothing. However, to Sarah's relief he began to carry her towards the couch. His face beamed with the pleasure of someone who has just won a lottery.

'When will Angela be home?' she asked as he set her down on the seat cushions and released her.

'Probably not until Sunday night. She thinks there might be a couple of possibilities for me in Melbourne. How are your toes?'

To her startled surprise, he whipped off her shoes, lifted her feet on to the up-ended coffee table and was gently massaging the stockinged toes of her right foot before Sarah could voice a reply. 'Should have put the knee in, you know. Much more effective than a kick to the shins.'

'And you mean to stay here in the apartment with me?' she squeaked. His fingers were doing funny things to the toes and sole of her foot, making her feel quite squirmish.

'All weekend,' he agreed. As if he sensed her dismay he looked up in surprise. 'Well, it is my apartment. It cost me quite a lot of money, but I can't imagine anyone I'd rather share it with. I know this weekend is going to be great,' he said with a conviction that Sarah was far from feeling.

He wriggled her toes a few more times, gave her sole a couple of playful taps, then straightened up, eyeing her with sparkling anticipation. 'Now I'll get you a drink. Do you good. Prepare you for what's coming, because there's a lot of things you don't understand.'

You could say that again, Sarah thought with some asperity.

'How about a sherry?' he suggested brightly. 'I saw a bottle in one of the kitchen cupboards.'

'Thank you.' Sarah couldn't find voice for any other words. Ben Haviland was not only big, he was positively overwhelming. She certainly needed a drink to restore some equilibrium. It had been a very rocky day, and she wasn't at all sure that the weekend ahead wouldn't be even rockier.

CHAPTER TWO

'I CAN see you're a very positive person,' Ben declared, smiling approval at Sarah as he handed her a glass tumbler full of sherry.

Either he knew nothing about sherry or he thought she was an alcoholic, Sarah mused, eyeing the huge amount of amber liquid in the glass. There was probably a third of a bottle in it. 'This is a very large sherry,' she observed drily, as he settled into the armchair opposite her.

'Yes,' he agreed, and grinned.

Somehow the grin was infectious. A smile tugged at the corners of Sarah's mouth. 'I'm not that positive. Or negative. Whichever way you want to look at it. I only ever drink in moderation,' she added, in case he had any bright ideas about getting her drunk.

'That's good!' he said with even more approval. 'We have a great deal in common, Sarah. More than you're aware of, but I'll come to that. I've got to take a chance and you could be it.'

'A chance at what?' she asked, wishing he wouldn't keep talking in riddles.

He nodded a couple of times in grave consideration. 'You're a real possibility, Sarah. In fact, I'm sure we could make it work. The more I think about it, the more certain I feel. And I always get this feeling when I'm on to something good.'

Sarah's pulse gave a little leap of apprehension. 'What do you mean . . . on to something good?' she demanded suspiciously. He might be Angela's brother but the growing warmth of his regard was very discomfiting. And his gaze was roving over her in an openly assessing manner.

Sarah knew she looked good. It was part of her job to present a fashionable image and she worked at it. Her black hair was layered into a sleek shape that hugged the back of her head and sliced down to longer bangs that followed the curve of her cheeks. She knew all the tricks of make-up; how to emphasise her grey-green eyes, highlight her cheekbones, shade the roundness of her jawline. She had a long neck, and the height to wear any clothes well, and she had worn one of Penny Walker's brilliant new designs today, as an additional selling point to her sales pitch at the conference. The knitted fabric hugged her figure and the vibrant combination of black, green and violet was an eye-stopper.

'Better than good,' said Ben, with rich satisfaction. 'Never felt more sure of anything.'

Which was no answer at all. He hitched himself forward with an air of eagerness. Sarah took a defensive sip of sherry and then a larger one to loosen a sudden tension in her stomach. She refused to feel intimidated, but Ben Haviland certainly was a big strong man. The way he had held Julian so effortlessly was proof of that.

He was also disturbingly masculine. Aggressively masculine. Somehow he made her feel extremely conscious of being a woman. She couldn't help noticing how the stretch fabric of his grey track suit had to do a lot of stretching across the powerfully muscled thighs, and that the broad shoulders completely blotted out the backrest of the armchair. However, his smile was reassuring. It was nothing but genial.

'Sarah, I know this will come as a shock to you, but I'm in a terrible dilemma and I reckon you're my best shot. What I want . . . what I need . . . is for you to marry me.'

To say she was stunned would have been the understatement of the year. After a few totally blank moments, Sarah's brain moved into sluggish gear. Either she hadn't heard right or Ben Haviland was definitely off his rocker. She gulped down a very large swig of sherry. The warm tingle of alcohol helped to jolt her thought processes along. Maybe it was a joke.

'Sorry, but you just saw me retire from the marriage stakes,' she said flippantly. 'The last thing I want in my life at present is a man. You'll have to find yourself another candidate.'

'You're really against marriage?' he queried seriously.

Sarah didn't want to think about it. If she did stop to consider what she had just done to her relationship with Julian, she would probably break down and cry for a week. But she certainly wasn't going to show her emotional distress to a stranger. She shot Ben Haviland a derisive look. 'You heard me spell it out to Julian. After what I've been through with him, I'm damned sure that marriage is a prison I don't wish to enter. Not with him, and certainly not with you.'

His face relaxed into another bright smile. 'You're so right. That's exactly how I feel about marriage. A suffocating prison.'

Sarah eyed him warily. Was he some kind of a nutcase? First he proposed marriage and in the next breath he was against it! Caution was in order, Sarah decided. At the first opportunity she would make a break for it and head home to her parents' place in the Blue Mountains. Staying in this apartment for the weekend was clearly out of the question. On Monday she would find out from Angela if her brother had ever been in a psychiatric institution. Meanwhile the sensible thing to do was humour him.

'Why are you against marriage?' she asked solemnly.

He winced and shook his head. 'I had the most dreadful experience. Worse than yours. I was almost at the altar when I finally realised how badly I'd been deceived. The woman I was going to marry had actually lined up a job for me and wanted me to take it. Can you imagine that? Thinking she could push me into work!'

He shuddered at the thought. 'And that was only the last straw. I won't bore you with the rest. I tell you, Sarah, there was only one thing to do. I ran. You might think that was cowardly, but if you knew the woman you'd understand. She wanted everything her way and me under her thumb. Couldn't even see my point of view.'

Like Julian, Sarah thought bitterly, although the position was somewhat reversed. It was Julian's dismissal of her job that had been the last straw, not a demand that she take one. Yet if Ben Haviland didn't work, how had he got the money to buy this apartment for Angela?

Again she eyed him warily. There was no doubt that he was eccentric, but he didn't look mad. His claim about owning this apartment could be right. The rent was almost ridiculously low. Sarah had always thought how terribly lucky she had been in answering Angela's advertisement for a flatmate. Such a well appointed apartment with harbour views could easily command double the amount she paid Angela each week.

Curiosity drove Sarah to pick her words carefully, not wanting to offend the big man. 'If you don't work, Ben, how did you raise the capital to buy this apartment?'

'Used my brains,' he answered promptly. Then seeing her incomprehension, he added, 'What I do is sell ideas. Perfectly natural for a guy who hates work as I do. As it happens, I'm fairly good at coming up with things that have appeal for the general public. Too good this time, which is why I've got the problem I have.'

His mouth turned down into a grimace. 'I've had the best lawyers and accountants in the country working on it and they all come up with the same answer. Get married. Split your income with your wife. There's really no viable alternative. I've got to do it, no matter what I feel. And time's running out. Today is the twentieth of May, and there are only forty-one days left. I must be married by the thirtieth of June.'

Sarah was completely lost in this line of logic, if indeed there was any line of logic. 'Why?' she asked, hoping to get a glimmer of light.

'Because it's the end of the financial year. If I'm not married by then, they're going to hit me hard, Sarah,' he said, shooting her a look of desperate appeal.

Sarah shook her head in bewilderment. 'Who's going to hit you hard?'

'The taxation department!' he spat out in disgust. 'It's a case of blatant discrimination. A married man can have a partnership and split his income, but an unmarried man has to bear double the burden. I don't mind paying my fair share. I do that anyway. I reckon I'm supporting half the welfare state as it is. But this is an absolute rip-off, Sarah, and the only way around it is to get married.'

Light dawned. Sarah heaved a sigh of relief. Ben Haviland wasn't mad at all. There was nothing mad about trying to hold on to a fair share of one's hard-earned cash. She offered him a sympathetic smile. 'Well, I'm sorry about your financial problems, but you can't really expect me to bail you out of them. It seems to me that marriage is a pretty drastic answer, particularly since you see it as a trap. Better to pay up and keep your freedom.'

He held up a hand and put on a grave face. 'You don't understand. Truly you don't. It's big money. Really big. All my chickens have come home to roost at the same time. I'm in desperate trouble. In the normal course of events I wouldn't think of proposing.'

The grave face slowly melted into a pleased grin as he relaxed back into the chair. His eyes sparkled absolute delight at her. 'But you and I, Sarah—that's something else again. We'd make the ideal partnership,' he said with relish.

Her heart gave a funny little lurch. She took several gulps of sherry to steady an oddly wayward pulse. There was a smug air of confidence about him that she wanted to prick. He had no right to be looking at her like that. It was presumptuous, and, God knew, she'd had enough of presumptuous men. After her experience with Julian, she doubted that she would ever trust another man in any relationship. Men didn't want to be partners with women. Not equal partners.

She fixed Ben Haviland with a sceptical eye. 'The last thing I need is another man to screw up my life. I've already been through that. The moment you let a man in your life, he starts making demands, and the longer the relationship goes on, the more demanding he becomes.'

'Same with a woman,' Ben said with feeling. 'They never know when to stop. Why can't they let a man be himself? Always trying to change him!'

His counter-claim stirred the boiling well of resentment that was still simmering inside her. 'Huh!' she responded scornfully. 'You don't even see the other side of the coin. Let me tell you what Julian did to me today . . .' And she spilled out the whole chain of events, reliving it again with vehement passion.

It was good to let it all out, and Ben Haviland was the perfect listener. He muttered sympathetic comments. His expressions mirrored her own feelings, apparently in absolute accord with the sentiments she was expressing. When she finally wound down he shook his head over the whole affair in appreciative understanding for all that she had suffered, and sat in sympathetic silence while they both contemplated the mean crimes some people perpetrated on others.

'You should have let me drop him out of the window,' Ben said finally. 'The whole trouble is, neither men nor women show their true colours until they think they've got you tied up.'

'Exactly,' Sarah sighed, and took another sip of sherry. Her throat was quite dry from all the talking she had done.

Ben Haviland was right, she decided. They did have a lot in common, and it was nice to have someone on a sympathetic wavelength with her, particularly after the terribly stressful day she had been through. She looked across at him and smiled, grateful for his company, however eccentric he was. He obviously took her smile as an encouraging signal for he began to argue his cause again.

'We wouldn't be like that, Sarah,' he said with firm conviction. 'Don't you see how ideal it is? Both of us want to live life on our own terms, and we can do it if we get together. It's the perfect arrangement. You'll have the financial security of being married to me and the Government can't bleed me white. It'll save us a lot of money, Sarah.

A lot of money. And don't think I won't be appreciative.'

Promises, promises, Sarah thought with all the bitterness of her recent disillusionment. While she now understood Ben's dilemma, she certainly didn't feel she wanted to be the answer to it. 'You're the one who has to get married. Not me,' she pointed out decisively. 'And I'm quite capable of supporting myself, thank you.'

She lifted her glass in a mocking toast to him and swallowed some more sherry, then realised she was beginning to feel a bit fuzzy in the head. She frowned down at the glass in her hand and saw that it was three parts empty. She had inadvertently drunk far more than she had intended. Annoyed with herself, she leaned over and placed the tumbler on the coffee table with a decisive bang.

Ben caught hold of her hand as she withdrew it from the glass. He had hitched himself forward again, and when she looked up, his face was quite close to hers and the blue eyes held a mesmerising intensity of purpose.

'Sarah ... how would you like to run your own boutique? Complete authority. Buy and sell whatever you like. Do whatever you want, whenever you want.'

It was her favourite daydream, although she knew it would never be possible because there was no way she could ever raise enough capital. Every week she took tickets in LOTTO in the faint hope that maybe one day she might get lucky and win the big first prize. That was her only chance of ever getting enough money to do what she wanted. One thing she did trust, however, was her instinct for what fashions would sell well, and she had no doubt that she could run a successful boutique.

'Sarah, I can give you the financial backing you need to run the best fashion boutique in Sydney. You can have a completely free hand to set up whatever you want. Everything you need. Cost no object. But I need a wife.'

She looked blankly at Ben, not quite taking in what he was offering. He bounced to his feet, and pulled her to hers as he swiftly rounded the coffee table. He let go her hand and gently cupped her face, forcing her attention.

'Any location you like. Double Bay, inner city . . . whatever fashion goods you want to sell. All you have to do is marry me before the thirtieth of June. A favour for a favour, Sarah. That's fair, isn't it?'

'You . . . you can't mean it,' she stammered disbelievingly.

'There's that much money involved in it, Sarah. Word of honour. Better still, I'll get my solicitor to write up a marriage contract setting out the terms. How's that?'

'But . . . I . . . I can't marry you just to . . . to . . .'

'Of course you can.' His hands dropped from her

face to slide around her waist and draw her closer to him. 'You're a free agent now. You can do anything you want. Jut think of it, Sarah. You can do your own thing with absolute authority. No money problems. No one dictating how you're to run your life. Our marriage wouldn't be a prison, Sarah.'

The future he was painting danced before her eyes, compellingly attractive, a fantasy of limitless possibilities. She stared up at him and felt caught in the excitement that lit his face.

'And there's nothing about you I'd want to change, Sarah,' he said emphatically. 'I think you're perfect, just as you are.'

And while Sarah was still trying to work some sanity into her befuddled mind, Ben translated his appreciation into more physical terms, his mouth descending on hers with a kiss that was startlingly persuasive in its sheer sensuality. Sarah hadn't meant to respond. In fact, one corner of her mind told her she should be properly outraged by the liberties he was taking with her person. It wasn't just the kiss. His embrace was drawing her closer and closer to him, making her terribly aware of the hard masculinity of his body. And his hands were caressing the curve of her spine with a gentle, knowing pressure that was both comforting and pleasurable.

Sarah made a valiant effort to focus her mind. This had to be stopped. This morning she had been engaged to Julian, and no matter how disaffected she was with him, to be accepting and responding to another man's kiss . . . and body . . . it just wasn't right. It had to be all that sherry . . . making her light-headed . . . or something. Reluctantly but determinedly she dragged her mouth away from his and turned her head aside, sucking in a deep, steadying breath before attempting to break the embrace.

Ben gave her little breathing space. His mouth moved to her ear and awakened a sensitivity that tingled through her whole body. 'Don't!' she gasped.

'Can't help it. It's your perfume drawing me on,' he murmured, caressing the long line of her throat with nibbling little kisses that totally seduced the protest on Sarah's tongue.

'*Impulse*,' she breathed, as if that explained everything.

'Very strong,' Ben agreed huskily, one hand roaming closer to the underswell of her breast.

'No. The perfume. It's called *Impulse*,' Sarah said on a shivery sigh. The hand had found an erotic line just under her armpit and really it was quite terrible how weakly receptive she was to its touch.

'Never felt more that way,' Ben murmured, moving her lower body to fit more intimately to his.

And that jolted Sarah back down to earth. Ben's

impulses were all too noticeably aroused. Shame shot through her like a bolt of lightning and jerked her out of his embrace. 'Stop!' she cried, in terrible agitation.

And he did stop. Abruptly. He pulled away and his face was a picture of hurt puzzlement at her vehement rejection.

'I'm sorry,' Sarah said limply. 'I shouldn't have let you do that. I don't know what got into me,' she babbled on, appalled at her uncharacteristic lapse of control.

'My fault,' Ben said in instant mitigation. 'I don't usually get carried away like that. Must have been a release of tension.'

'Yes,' she agreed quickly. It certainly had been a tense day.

'Fresh air. That's what we need. And a good solid meal. That'll clear our heads for serious planning. Let's go for a stroll and find a restaurant.'

Sarah couldn't get her shoes on fast enough. She didn't even consider what serious planning Ben had in mind. She just wanted to escape from the disturbing intimacy that had been generated in this apartment. He held the door open for her and she slipped past him quickly, far too physically aware of him even to meet his eyes.

'Angela said there's quite a good restaurant only a couple of blocks away,' Ben remarked as they rode down in the elevator.

'Yes,' said Sarah, choked by his nearness. The compartment seemed terribly small with Ben Haviland in it. She shook her head, trying to shake off the strange influence that he was having on her. She had never felt anything like it before in her whole life. 'Being with you is like riding on a roller-coaster,' she said ruefully.

He smiled a heart-catching smile. 'There's no one I'd rather ride with.'

Sarah felt hopelessly confused by her unwarranted reaction to him. 'You're going too fast,' she protested, almost panicking at the strange magnetism that was pulling her along with him.

'Time is the enemy,' he declared blithely, and caught her hand as they walked out of the apartment block.

She shot him an apprehensive glance, wondering if she was being incredibly foolish to accompany him anywhere when she was obviously not her usual sensible self. 'I haven't said I'll marry you,' she reminded him, but she left her hand in his. There was something rather nice about the way he held it. Firm, yet somehow caring. She liked it. It was friendly.

They walked one block in silence.

'I wouldn't make demands on you, Sarah,' Ben said seriously. 'If we're not in mutual agreement about something, then you go your way and I'll go mine. No argument. No pressures. OK?'

'OK,' she echoed, then berated herself for the unthinking agreement.

How could she marry a man she hardly knew? The idea was preposterous. On the other hand, what kind of future did she have to look forward to? Another thirty years in the department store, having her ideas stultified by people like Frances Chatfield? If she had her own boutique ... and, after all, it was really a business partnership she would have with Ben. Nothing personal.

The hand holding hers instantly mocked that last idea. And what had already happened between them mocked it even more. 'This marriage you want ... you aren't actually considering us living together, are you?' she asked, staring straight ahead as she felt a flush of embarrassment creeping up her neck. 'That's a hypothetical question, of course,' she added firmly.

'Well ... er ... very tricky things, hypothetical questions.' He paused a long time before answering her. 'Actually, I think that depends very much on the two people concerned, although living together is the usual situation when one gets married,' he finished matter-of-factly.

Sarah took a deep breath. 'I meant ... would you ... would you expect to go to bed with me?'

Again there was a long pause before he spoke, and when he did, it was even more hesitantly. 'Well—er ... what ... er ...' He took a deep breath.

'Umm . . . were you planning on being celibate for the rest of your life, Sarah?'

Which was a very tricky question. 'I'd have to think about it,' she muttered.

'Ah,' he said, and fell silent for another half a block. His fingers fondled hers as if he was in deep thought. Sarah couldn't bring herself to look at him. It really was terribly shameless the way she had responded to him. He probably thought she was promiscuous, which wasn't the case at all.

Ben suddenly stopped dead and turned to her with an air of decision. 'I won't lie to you. I certainly want to go to bed with you, Sarah. Can't deny it. In fact I can't remember when I ever felt so attracted to a woman. But that doesn't mean you have to go to bed with me. I'll respect your wishes. Any time you don't want to go to bed with me, all you have to do is say so. Fair enough?'

'Yes,' she said quickly, feeling a bewildering wave of relief. Was she relieved because he wanted her to share his bed . . . or because she didn't have to? Sarah shook her head over the idea as they resumed walking. She wasn't a sex-orientated person. Although she had found Julian's lovemaking quite pleasurable, at times, she had never initiated it. Nor had she craved for it. In fact, she didn't think she would even miss it.

But the rest of her life was a different matter, she argued to herself. She mightn't want to stay celibate, and if she accepted Ben's proposal ... which she wouldn't! It was crazy even to consider it. She sneaked a quick sideways glance at him. In a purely physical sense he was a very attractive man. Big, but very well proportioned. If he was her husband, she didn't think she'd mind going to bed with him. The way he had kissed her ... he was surely very, very good at making love.

'How old are you?' she blurted out.

'Thirty-four,' he answered promptly. 'And you?'

'Twenty-eight.'

'That's good!' he said in some relief. 'Actually you look younger. It worried me a bit.'

'Why?'

'I wouldn't like to think I was taking advantage of a young girl on the rebound, so to speak. But you impressed me as a woman who knows her own mind, Sarah. And speaks it. You're a very positive person. I like that. I like that very much.'

And his hand squeezed hers. Rather possessively, Sarah thought, but found she didn't mind.

They reached the restaurant and were lucky enough to find a table free. Ben ordered a bottle of champagne with their meal.

'I really can't marry you,' Sarah insisted when the waiter had departed.

His smile was slow and very warm. 'I feel like

champagne. Tell me all about yourself and your family.'

With the change of subject Sarah relaxed. 'I have three older brothers, all married with families. I'm the only girl and a terrible disappointment to my mother. She wants to see me married like the others.'

The thought brought an abrupt stab of guilt. 'Poor Mum! She's going to be upset with me, breaking my engagement with Julian. She and Dad were looking forward to meeting him. We were supposed to go up to Mount Victoria tomorrow afternoon and stay the weekend with them.' Her smile was full of bitter irony. 'For a discussion of wedding plans. But now . . .' Her hands fluttered in a gesture of hopelessness.

'Won't I do instead?' Ben asked.

She was startled by the offer. 'But—but you wouldn't want a proper wedding and—and all that goes with it!'

'Who said that? I don't mind. As long as we get married, I don't care how we do it. Might as well make your parents happy.'

'What about your parents?'

He shrugged. 'They gave up on me years ago. Nothing I do will surprise them. Apart from which they're overseas and won't be back for months.'

The bottle of champagne arrived along with their first course. Sarah was glad of something to eat. She was feeling distinctly light-headed. She wondered if she was mad enough to contemplate marriage with Ben Haviland, then decided that mad or not, she *would* contemplate it.

A smile tugged at her mouth. Everyone would think it a very odd marriage, but it was really nobody's business but hers and Ben's. And if Ben was willing to humour her parents, well, it was more than Julian had been willing to do. She wondered how Angela would react, and the thought prompted the question.

'What does Angela think about this marriage scheme?'

A surprisingly sheepish look flitted over Ben Haviland's face. 'She's ... umm ... working on it for me. I didn't know I was going to meet you, Sarah,' he added quickly.

The absurdity of the situation suddenly hit Sarah. She began to laugh, and when the laughter finally rippled down to a grin, she asked, 'How old were you when you almost made it to the altar the first time?'

'Twenty-four. And you can laugh, Sarah Woodley, but I can tell you it was deadly serious. Put me off the idea of marriage altogether. That woman was going to swallow me whole and chew me into little pieces,' he declared feelingly.

Sarah began to giggle again. 'She'd have to have a big mouth.'

'About as big as Julian's, I'd say,' he shot at her testily.

Sarah immediately sobered. He was right. If she had gone along with Julian, he would have swallowed her whole and chewed her into little pieces. 'I'm sorry,' she sighed as depression nibbled at her again.

'No, *I'm* sorry,' Ben said softly, and she looked up into kind, compassionate eyes. 'I've just remembered how bad I felt at the time. I guess you feel pretty bad, too. I wish I didn't have to rush you, Sarah, but I really haven't got any alternative.'

He was nice. A bit wacky, but nice. She smiled. 'Well, at least you've been very successful at distracting me from more miserable thoughts.'

'And you'll marry me?' he pressed eagerly.

For a moment Sarah thought—why the hell not? What did she have to lose? Any marriage was a gamble and this one would at least let her be herself. Ben was handing her the opportunity of a lifetime as far as a work situation was concerned. She would be a fool to turn it down. But could she live with the decision? It seemed so mercenary and cold-blooded.

'I'll think about it.'

'Please?'

The intense appeal in his eyes seemed very personal, not cold-blooded or mercenary at all. It muddled up her reasoning and she found herself thinking that she had lived very amicably with Angela for two years. And Ben was Angela's brother. Not that that meant anything, but ... maybe it could work very well. She imagined him always sitting across from her at the table. Her husband. He was certainly very attractive.

'It's a temptation,' she said slowly.

Happy relief spread across his face. 'That's great! Now we're getting somewhere. I knew you were a positive person, Sarah.'

'I haven't given you a positive answer,' she pointed out.

'Not yet,' he agreed, but his smile looked very confident as he filled her glass with champagne.

CHAPTER THREE

WAS she really taking Ben Haviland's proposal seriously, Sarah mused several times throughout the meal, or was it simply a pipe-dream that was far easier to contemplate than the inevitable consequences of today's events? She felt light-headed and heavy-hearted at the same time—probably the effect of all the sherry and champagne.

She watched, a little pie-eyed as Ben topped up her glass again. Some persistent threads of common sense told her she shouldn't drink any more, but she couldn't be bothered to voice a protest. What did it matter? What did anything matter?

Ben Haviland had nice eyes. They were like Angela's, open and honest, and she liked the way he was looking at her, as if she were a real prize, someone worth having. It proved that Julian was wrong with his arrogant claim that he was probably her last chance at marriage. Ben would have her tonight if she said yes. He found her desirable enough to go along with whatever she wanted.

But she didn't love him. She didn't love him and he didn't love her, and even though he was laying at her feet a bridge to a new kind of life, she would be a fool to rely on it. She had been a fool to rely on Julian. It should be Julian sitting opposite her now, giving her the support that Ben was giving. Instead of that, Julian had uncaringly activated her defeat by that bitch, Frances Chatfield. Julian, who had said he loved her . . .

'Sarah, are you all right?'

The caring note in Ben's voice tripped her heart. The tears that had welled into her eyes made his face a blur but she could see he was leaning towards her in a pose of concern. She shook her head and blinked hard but the tears kept coming.

'It's been a hell of a day,' she confessed miserably.

'I'll get the bill. Take you home,' he said, quickly reacting to her need, his voice soft and his hand reaching across the table to press hers sympathetically.

He was as good as his word. Their waiter was immediately summoned, the bill disposed of in moments, and Ben was on his feet, helping Sarah to hers. His arm curled around her shoulders and it was comforting to lean her weight on him as he steered her to the exit. Once outside both of his arms came around her and Sarah was gently turned to face him.

'Why are you crying?'

'I'm not,' she denied, but she could not meet his eyes.

He lightly pressed her head on to his shoulder and his cheek rubbed over her hair. Sarah felt too worn out to resist and there was no threat in Ben's embrace. The warm strength of him enveloped her, supported her, made her feel cherished, and she desperately needed some cherishing.

'It's all right, Sarah,' he whispered. 'I won't let anyone hurt you. Ever again.'

The temptation to give up, to surrender herself into his keeping, was almost overwhelming in that moment of weakness. It felt right. Better to marry him than a lot of others. Possibly anyone. He would do more for her than most, and he didn't expect her to pamper his ego. Maybe love was only an illusion anyway. An understanding partnership was probably a more sensible foundation on which to build a purposeful future.

Ben hailed a passing taxi and bundled her into the back seat with him. 'We can walk. It's only a few blocks,' Sarah expostulated.

'You're dead on your feet. I'm taking you home the quickest way possible,' Ben replied, and gave the address to the cab driver.

The taxi pulled up outside the apartment block in a matter of moments and it seemed perfectly natural to lean on Ben as he helped her out. He hugged her close to him during the elevator ride up to the fourth floor and only let her go to usher her into the apartment after he had unlocked the door.

'Ben! Is that you?' Angela came charging out of the kitchen, her face alight with triumph. The change of expression was almost comic as she goggled at the pair of them, Sarah's head drooping against Ben's shoulder and his arm almost encircling her waist. 'What are you two doing together?' she demanded in startled surprise.

Sarah simply stared, her befuddled head only slowly coming to grips with Angela's unexpected appearance on the scene. It was Ben who voiced her thought.

'What are you doing back here? You're supposed to be in Melbourne,' he said on a critical note.

'Mission accomplished,' Angela retorted, eyeing her brother with some exasperation. 'And the least I expected of you was to remain where I could find you.'

Ben shrugged off the criticism. 'Just took Sarah out for a meal.'

Angela frowned at Sarah. 'I thought you'd be out with Julian.' The frown cleared as she added, 'But I'm glad you don't find my brother too objectionable. I was . . .'

'That's enough of that, Angela,' Ben cut in irritably.

She heaved a sigh and shook her head at her big brother as if he were a recalcitrant child. 'Just don't come to me for sympathy when this mad scheme of yours brings you grief.'

'It's not mad. Some of the best brains in the country advised me ...'

'I know. I know. But only you would try to get around it this way. Any normal person ...'

'Look who's calling the kettle black! If you were a normal woman, you wouldn't be a crime reporter.'

'I like reporting crime,' Angela said indignantly.

'And I like ...'

Sarah drifted to the nearest armchair and sat down. Her head felt dizzy. Angela and Ben were too involved in their argument to notice that she had removed herself from the field of battle. She watched them rave on at each other, noting there was no real animosity in their manner or speech. It was the kind of spat a brother and sister can enjoy with each other, familiarity and affection ensuring that there were no hard feelings left on either side.

Apart from their eyes, they shared little similarity in appearance. Angela was barely average height and rather petite in figure. Her hair might have been the same brown colour as Ben's but she regularly had blonde streaks put through it. This was to add more individuality to what she called her ordinary looks. She was pretty without being striking, and her pet hatred was other people observing that she reminded them of someone else.

She was not the least bit daunted by her brother's size, and a smile tugged at Sarah's mouth as Angela adopted her belligerent pose: hands on hips, chin lifted, eyebrows arched in scornful challenge. 'At least I know where I'm heading,' she declared loftily.

'And so do I!' Ben retorted with vehement authority.

'Huh!' scoffed Angela and put on a cynical smile. 'Then you should be grateful to me, Ben. I've found someone who will go through this charade of a marriage with you.'

That jolted Sarah out of her passive daze. It also pulled Ben up short. He shot an axious look at her then frowned heavily at his sister.

'Er ... matter of fact, Angela, I've found the woman I want myself. Not that I'm ungrateful for what you've done, but ...'

'Oh, that's great, that is!' Angela sniped at him. 'Now I'm left looking an absolute fool. As if it wasn't bad enough that I had to play the part of a shifty marriage agent ...'

The burst of indignation floated over Sarah's head. One word was echoing through her mind with devastating force... charade... a charade of a marriage ... and, of course, that was what it would be. No love, no substance to it, a pretence, just as Ben's caring for her tonight had probably been a pretence to get what he wanted. Suddenly the depression that his diverting company had kept at bay, descended on her with a vengeance. She rose stiffly to her feet and pasted a brittle smile on her face.

'Well, you won't be needing me any more, Ben. I'm sure Angela's candidate will fit the bill. If you'll both excuse me, I'd like to retire.'

Ben's hand flew out to detain her, his face a study in sincere appeal. 'Hold on, Sarah. I don't want to marry anyone else. No one could be better than you.'

'Sarah?' Angela's voice was an incredulous squawk. 'Now I know you're out of your mind, Ben. Sarah's already engaged to be married and she'd never——'

'We got rid of him,' Ben threw at her impatiently. 'Sarah and I are in total agreement about marriage. It's a fool's game and we're smart enough to——'

'What do you mean, you got rid of him?' Angela's mouth dropped open in horror as she turned to Sarah. 'My God! He hasn't messed things up with Julian, has he? I'll never forgive myself for leaving him here. I thought I could trust Ben to behave himself for once.'

'Dammit, Angela! I *did* behave myself,' Ben exploded in exasperation. 'I didn't throw him out of the window. I didn't even kick him out of the door. I let him go peaceably, just as Sarah said.'

'Oh, God!' Angela turned frantic eyes of apology

back to Sarah. 'I'll do whatever I can to fix it. I'm so sorry. So——'

Sarah stepped out of Ben's light grasp and gave her friend's arm a reassuring squeeze. 'It's all right, Angela. I called it off with Julian and he didn't take it well. I'm grateful to Ben for stepping in when he did. It saved me a nasty scene.'

Angela searched her eyes worriedly. 'You called it off, Sarah? But you've been crazy about him.'

Sarah heaved a sadly ironic sigh. 'Crazy stupid, I guess. Anyhow, it's over.'

'But why?' Angela shook her head, mystified, then in a burst of anxious concern, 'Well, whatever happened, you can't be crazy enough to take Ben on, Sarah! That's not what you want.'

'Hey! Whose side are you on, Angela?' Ben protested loudly.

'No, it's not what I want,' Sarah agreed dully. The tears gathered again and she blundered off down the hallway to her bedroom, needing quite desperately to nurse her heartache in private.

'Sarah!' Ben called after her.

'You leave her alone, you ... you numskull!' Angela berated him.

'You don't understand ...'

'If you think for one minute that Sarah's the type to—to sell herself to you, you're a bigger fool than I thought you were!'

'You've got it all wrong. We'd be partners, not——'

Sarah closed her door on the argument. Angela didn't have it wrong, she thought, sickened by the stark truth of the bargain she had almost made with Ben. He would have been buying her. She had even gone so far as to think of sharing her bed with him. Shame added its sting to her tears. She dragged off her clothes and climbed into bed, welcoming the darkness and the soft muffling of her pillow in which to bury her misery.

She didn't want the empty charade of a marriage that Ben offered. She wanted what Julian had promised, the sharing of their lives within the bond of love. She could tell herself she had been stupid and blind to ignore the way their relationship had been heading. She could tell herself she had been right to end it, but the hurt could not be dismissed quite so easily. A whole year of emotional involvement would not be cut dead. Julian had answered a lot of needs in Sarah that would not suddenly go away.

There were many pleasures they had enjoyed sharing: a love of dancing, skiing, dining out with friends. She had been proud of the way he could handle any social situation. He had been proud of her flair for fashion. They had looked good together and there had been a lot of social advantages in being an established couple. All gone now, Sarah mourned, and wondered if she had been a fool to throw it all away.

Maybe Julian had been right, and her job didn't matter. Was it her ego at fault, too wrapped up in a career position it had taken ten years to achieve? But it wasn't only Julian's arrogant lack of consideration over that, Sarah reminded herself. It was an ingrained attitude on his part, that had been chafing her for some time. Everthing would be fine as long as she went along with what Julian wanted. But how long could she have gone on swallowing her resentment at his cavalier dismissal of her wishes for the sake of peace between them? For a lifetime?

And it had been getting worse—Julian taking her submission to his selfish will more and more for granted. And he couldn't, or wouldn't even see that he was wrong. That was what made her so mad, so frustrated and . . . No, she couldn't have lived with it. Not in the long run. That wasn't her idea of love or of how a relationship should work between people who respected each other. It was too one-sided. Suffocatingly one-sided.

The tap on her door jerked Sarah's head up from the pillow, but the quick recognition of Angela's familiar silhouette brought relief even before her friend spoke. 'Mind if I come in for a minute?'

'No, I don't mind,' Sarah assured her carelessly, and dropped her head back on the pillow.

Angela swiftly closed the door and tactfully chose not to switch on the light. She felt her way along the bed and Sarah shifted her position to make room for her friend to sit down.

'Sarah ...' Angela sucked in a deep breath and continued in a guilty rush, 'Ben tells me I was out of line saying what I did, and it's none of my business what you choose to do with your life, and if you think marrying Ben is a good move, well ... that's your decision, and I'm sorry I butted my nose in and ...'

'Angela, stop worrying,' Sarah advised as soon as she could get a word in. 'It was just a silly dream. Reaction to the break-up with Julian, I suppose. Ben was here and——' she shook her head over her odd receptivity to Ben's proposal '—I guess I was in the mood to listen. He was nice to me.'

Very nice ... the way he had held her, looked at her, talked to her, kissed her ... it hadn't felt like a charade. But how could she trust her feelings after her terrible mistake with Julian?

Angela still sounded uncertain as she pressed on. 'Well, Ben isn't too pleased with me at the present moment. Said I insulted you and he really means to look after you and treat you right.'

'He did look after me tonight,' Sarah conceded with a whimsical little smile. 'But it won't do, Angela. I'd want more from a husband than just money. I'm sorry I led Ben to think I might be interested.'

Angela heaved a huge sigh of relief. 'Well, thank God for that! Not that I wouldn't like you as my sister-in-law, Sarah, but much as I love my brother, I'm damned sure he'd make you a terrible husband. He's quite mad, you know.'

'Mad?' The word recalled her initial doubts about Ben's sanity.

'I don't mean he's off his brain. Far from it. In fact, I guess a lot of people would call him a genius in a quirky kind of way. He's terribly clever but he's hopelessly erratic. Not the type you could ever hope to settle down with and lead any kind of normal existence. He's always on the move. He only arrived back from the States yesterday, and he's sure to take off again once he gets himself married. Even the thought of being pinned down horrifies him.'

Angela's voice suddenly warmed with affection as she added, 'That's not to say he doesn't have any virtues. Ben is wonderfully kind and generous. A real sucker for lame dogs and anybody who's got anything wrong with them.'

That would make sense, thought Sarah wryly. Tonight she had been a lame dog, and that probably explained why Ben had done all he could to make her feel better.

Angela sighed again. 'I'm sorry, Sarah. I've been

prattling on about Ben, when all you care about is Julian. I'm so sorry that . . . is it final?'

Sarah's answer was slow in coming, regret for what had been lost mixing with the bitterness of defeat. 'He'd have to change an awful lot for me to reconsider, Angela, and that's most unlikely. I'd rather not talk about it now.' The tears were gathering again.

'Sure,' Angela said in soft sympathy and quickly rose to her feet. 'I'll go and straighten my brother out. Don't worry about Ben, Sarah. I'll keep him out of your way. You just get a good night's sleep.'

Better for her to keep out of Ben's way too, Sarah thought when she was left alone. She had unwittingly encouraged him tonight, raised expectations that now had firmly to be set aside. She would pack a bag in the morning and catch a train to Mount Victoria after work. Her parents were expecting her . . . with Julian. The least she could do was got home and explain, try to mollify her mother's disappointment.

Mental and emotional exhaustion finally dragged Sarah into sleep. When she rose in the morning, she found that Angela had had the foresight to give her own room to her brother and had set up the foldaway bed for herself in the living-room. Sarah was grateful that she was saved the embarrassment of facing Ben again before she left. She told Angela her plans, asked her to wish

Ben luck with his marriage quest, then hurried out of the apartment before the man himself put in an appearance.

Saturday morning was always busy in the Young Trends department and Sarah was glad to be busy. She enjoyed advising customers on how to co-ordinate their chosen purchase with other mix-and-match garments. She was a good saleswoman, never pressing her suggestions but making sure the customer saw all that could be fancied and bought.

She was still smiling her satisfaction over a very large sale when Ashley Thompson, her best sales assistant, ventured a comment between customers. 'I guess we didn't get the Penny Walker contract.'

Sarah's smile turned into a grimace. 'No. Sorry, Ashley. I didn't feel like talking about it yesterday.'

The girl shared Sarah's own enthusiasm for the young designer's work and showed her disappointment. 'I bet that was Mrs Chatfield's doing.'

'Not all of it,' Sarah answered honestly. Then, on a more diplomatic note, 'No one accepts change easily, Ashley.'

Sarah suddenly caught sight of Julian striding purposefully towards her. Her mouth compressed to a thin line that barely held in a surge of rebellion. He wore a contemptuous air for the whole female fashion business. However, before he reached Sarah, she was approached by another customer for advice and she took secret satisfaction in the fact that Julian was forced into waiting for her attention.

But he didn't wait. In his arrogantly demanding way he broke into the conversation and directed that the customer go to Ashley, who was still at the sales desk. Rather than involve a customer in an unpleasant scene, Sarah let Ashley take over, but it took all her control to turn to Julian with an air of sang-froid.

'Another urgent and important matter, Julian?' she bit out.

'The question of our future is certainly urgent and important,' he retorted, a cold, stiff anger behind every word.

'We have no future, Julian. I thought I made that clear yesterday.'

'That's ridiculous, Sarah. We've got too much going for us for you to turn your nose up at it, so just climb down from your high horse and start talking sense.'

Her hackles rose to a dangerous peak. He was doing it to her again, putting her in the wrong instead of recognising his own shortcomings. 'Why don't *you* climb down, Julian?' she said with false sweetness. 'I'm rather sick of that little exercise.'

'Me climb down?' he snorted impatiently. 'I don't have to. It's you who's in a childish pet! It's about time you got your priorities straight, Sarah. If you're going to marry me——'

'But I'm not going to marry you,' she said flatly, aware now that he was never going to see her point of view.

His face contorted with frustration and Sarah could almost hear the grinding of teeth as he snarled, 'I'm not going to beg, Sarah. Please reconsider before it's too late.'

It cost her considerable effort simply to remain civil, but she tried to moderate the tone of her reply. 'I'm sorry, Julian, but we see things too differently. Thank you, but I really don't want another chance. It's better for both of us if we go our separate ways. Now, please excuse me. I have customers to attend to.'

He grasped her arm as she started to turn away and his fingers bit in hard. 'Stuff the customers!'

'Let go of me, Julian,' she demanded, her eyes as cold as a winter storm.

His mouth thinned into a cruel line.

Sarah barely controlled a tremor of fear. 'This is my territory and I'll have you ejected if you start making trouble,' she warned.

A hand suddenly clamped on Julian's arm. 'This guy giving you trouble again, Sarah?'

Startled, she looked up to find Ben Haviland standing at her shoulder. He looked impressive, dressed up in a dark business suit, spotless white shirt and a smart tie, and his genial face was set in beetling disapproval of Julian. Relief swept through Sarah. It felt good to have Ben beside her, ready to champion her cause.

'Nothing I can't handle,' she declared, confident that the situation would now be very quickly resolved.

Julian let her go and wrenched his arm out of Ben's grip. 'Don't think you can manhandle me in a public place. I'll have you up for assault,' he threatened.

'Then leave Sarah alone,' Ben said reasonably.

'Just who do you think you are?' Julian snarled, bristling for a fight.

Another misjudgement, Sarah thought in dismay. Julian's ego had taken too much of a bashing, and pride was forcing him to make a stand, despite the unequal odds. And customers were gathering around, staring curiously at them, listening to all that was going on. The need to end the unpleasant scene pounded through Sarah's mind and she pounced on the one sure solution. She could explain to Ben later, she assured herself as she consciously leaned against him.

'I'm sorry, Julian, but this is the man I'm going to marry,' she declared without batting an eyelash.

Julian's jaw sagged.

'You are?' Ben said, hopeful delight leaping into his eyes as he glanced down at her in surprise.

'There are conditions,' she hissed out of the side of her mouth. She hadn't realised he would look so eager and pleased. A flock of uncertainties played havoc with her heart.

'You can't marry him,' Julian thundered.

Sarah dragged her attention back to her ex-fiancé. He was glaring at her in terrible anger. She hoped the course she had so impulsively taken was not going to backfire on her and inspire an even worse scene.

'Yes, I can,' she insisted with ringing conviction, alarmingly aware that she had made her bed and now must lie in it, at least until Julian departed.

'She certainly can,' Ben said even more emphatically, his arm curving around Sarah's shoulders in pleased possession. 'This is great, Sarah,' he beamed down at her, blissfully ignoring Julian's presence. 'I told Angela she was wrong. Had to be. You and I . . .'

'I don't believe it!' Julian raged. 'Yesterday you were marrying me. Who is this guy, anyway?'

'Don't you know when to give up?' Ben shot at him. 'You had your chance and blew it. You're twenty-four hours too late. Now you haven't got any business here any more, and Sarah and I have arrangements to make, so just be a good chap and shove off. I don't want to hurt you.'

Julian's fists clenched as he glared hatred at both of them. The argument had drawn even more customers, fascinated with what would transpire next. Sarah's heart plummeted. What had possessed her to use Ben to fend off Julian? It had seemed like the inspiration of the moment until Ben had taken her literally at her word. Now she was going to have to find some way to square it with him.

'What time do you finish work, Sarah? Twelve o'clock?' he asked eagerly.

'Yes,' she replied, and was appalled to see Frances Chatfield's tight face of authority boring towards them. Julian was still standing his ground, furious and flummoxed. The situation was getting worse by the second.

'Then I'll pick you up the minute you're finished and we'll whiz off to Mount Victoria,' Ben said with satisfaction.

'I have to talk to you first, Ben,' Sarah got in hastily.

Julian exploded into absolute outrage. 'You're taking him up to meet your parents?' He shook a furious finger at her. 'That's it, Sarah! You're finished!'

His face was white. He was almost frothing at the mouth. To Sarah's intense relief he flung himself away, shouldering customers aside. He ran straight into Frances Chatfield. The bump he gave her knocked her to the floor. She gave a little cry of horror and distaste as she went down, and customers quickly gathered around to help her up. When she reappeared on her feet, the expression on her face would have turned Medusa to stone.

Sarah glanced up at Ben to find his attention focused entirely on herself and apparently unaware of any disturbance, but Sarah was instantly and forcefully imbued with the principle that discretion was the better part of valour. She spoke with sharp urgency. 'You'd better go, Ben. We can't talk now.' Time to explain to him later.

'No problem,' he said. 'Just tell me which exit you use.' He gave her no time to answer, his words tumbling on in happy anticipation. 'Better make it George Street. I'll go and buy a car straightaway. What do you fancy, Sarah? A Porsche? Jaguar? Ferrari? You'd look good in a Ferrari.'

A Ferrari? Her mind boggled for a moment and into that fraction of a pause sliced the waspish voice of Frances Chatfield.

'Ben Haviland! Finally putting in an appearance! And to find you in the midst of a disgraceful brawl is precisely what I'd expect.'

Ben's jaw dropped. His face stiffened in shock as he turned to meet the flinty gaze of Sarah's immediate superior. 'Frances!' The name was a strangled sound of horror.

'Yes. It's me.' It was a venomous hiss. The supercilious expression that Frances Chatfield usually wore had come unstuck and for the first time Sarah saw naked emotion glittering in her cold, beady eyes. The sight wasn't pretty. It gave

Sarah a crawly feeling down her spine.

Ben's face had gone white. He threw a hunted look at Sarah. 'Got to go. Wait for me, Sarah. At twelve o'clock. I'll be there.'

He was backing away even as he spoke in agitated bursts. His eyes kept darting at Frances as if he expected her to attack him. He threw one last look of frantic appeal at Sarah, then plunged off down the aisle to the nearest exit.

Frances Chatfield's mask of cool sophistication slipped back into place. She gave Sarah a look of scathing superiority. 'May I suggest, Miss Woodley, that as head of this department you show a very poor example by neglecting the firm's business in order to conduct your private affairs? I shall be giving a full report of this disgraceful incident. You deserve to be demoted. I will do my best to see that justice is done.'

Her voice dripped with acid scorn as she added, 'As for Ben Haviland, he is irresponsible, unreliable, and a reckless, amoral scoundrel, and it shows extremely poor judgement on your part to have become involved with him in any way whatsoever.'

With a disdainful lift of her chin she swung on her heel and sailed back to her own department. Sarah had to restrain an extremely childish urge to poke out her tongue. Any sympathy she might have felt for Frances Chatfield over Julian's nasty knock had been more than nullified by the mean vindictiveness of the woman. Not only had she spitefully sabotaged the Penny Walker contract, but there was no doubt that she would indeed do her best to see that Sarah lost her position.

It wasn't fair! Although it was probably her own fault, Sarah conceded grimly. If she hadn't been a blind idiot over Julian . . . if she hadn't brought Ben into the argument this morning . . . and how was she going to undo that?

A group of giggling teenagers caught her eye. They had been the group closest to the whole scene and obviously had been thoroughly entertained by it. One of them broke away and skipped over to Sarah as the others giggled at her audacity.

'Don't take any notice of that old battleaxe,' the girl advised. 'We reckon you should take the Ferrari and go.'

And before Sarah could make any comment, the group surged away, throwing cheeky backward glances as they convulsed with laughter. Sarah wished she could laugh, but what had started as a stupid impulse had finished up with far from funny consequences.

Now she had to face up to Ben and tell him she hadn't meant what she said. If he really did go off and buy a Ferrari . . . well, that wouldn't really be her fault, would it? Life was suddenly very complicated. And what was Ben's connection to Frances Chatfield that she should have such a shattering effect on him?

The name hadn't startled him last night when Sarah had told him about the conference. But Chatfield was Frances's married name. If Ben had known her . . . Sarah recalled that Frances had been Frances Upshot ten years ago and she wasn't really old. About thirty-eight. Could she have been the woman who had niggled Ben with more and more demands until he had bolted? She certainly was the type, and he had certainly bolted when confronted by her.

Sarah could not help chuckling over the incident in retrospect. Ben had taken to his heels as if threatened by a ravening wolf. He would have fought Julian, or any man, without turning a hair, but faced with Frances . . . The irony of the situation suddenly struck her—Julian and herself, Ben and Frances. Maybe she and Ben should team up to protect each other against the tyrants of the world. 'Take the Ferrari and go.' But that was being hopelessly fanciful, Sarah thought with a heavy sigh.

She glanced at her watch. Nine-fifty-six. Two more hours before she could set Ben straight. She hoped he wouldn't be too angry with her when she explained that she couldn't marry him after all. No, he wouldn't be angry, she decided. He'd understand. But she felt awful about disappointing him again.

CHAPTER FOUR

SARAH was not familiar with Ferraris, but when the ultra-sleek red sports car pulled into the kerb near the George Street exit of the store, its sophisticated lines left her in no doubt as to its identity. It shocked her. She hadn't really believed that Ben would do it, or even could do it. It didn't seem possible that anyone could just go and buy a Ferrari off the rack, so to speak. But there was Ben in the driver's seat, tooting the horn and waving her forward with hurry-up gestures.

She snapped herself out of the incredulous daze and moved. Ben had the passenger door open for her by the time she reached it and she passed him the overnight bag she had packed. He heaved it on to the back seat and grinned happily at her as she dropped into the low-slung, beautifully moulded leather seat.

'Like it?' he asked, reaching across for her seat-belt and fastening it for her.

'How did you get it?' The question was still whirling through her mind.

'A sale is a sale. I simply told them if they wanted to sell it, it had to be ready for me to hit the road by a quarter to twelve.' And he proceeded to hit the road, moving smoothly into the stream of traffic heading down George Street.

'But . . . but how did you pay for it?' She still couldn't believe it, even though she was actually riding in the car.

'Credit card, of course,' he smiled, as if any old credit card could buy a Ferrari. 'Hope your mother likes chocolates. And I didn't know what your father's favourite drink is so I bought him a good bottle of whisky, a good bottle of cognac and a good bottle of port.' He flashed her a self-satisfied grin. 'How's that?'

Sarah felt even more awful. He had done all this for her because she had said she was going to marry him and now . . . Now she had to tell him it had been a stupid, defensive lie. 'You shouldn't have done that, Ben,' she began in a very small voice, but Ben didn't give her time to continue.

'No trouble. I thought your mother would like to see a ring on your finger, too. I should have got your finger size but I didn't want to run the risk of running into Frances again . . .' His mouth set in a grim line and he gave a brief shake of his head. 'I'd sooner face piranhas. Or crocodiles. That woman is a viper, Sarah.'

'You don't have to tell me that,' Sarah said with feeling. 'I've had ten years of working under her.

She's the Frances Chatfield I told you about last night.'

'Chatfield? You mean she's married?'

'Widowed.'

'That'd make sense,' Ben said grimly. 'She probably poisoned her husband like she poisoned my dog.'

'She did that?' Sarah was shocked, yet on second thoughts she didn't have much difficulty in believing that Frances Chatfield could poison a dog. 'Was she the woman who almost got you to marry her, Ben?'

'She's the one. God knows, I was a terrible fool to ever get so deeply involved with her. Somehow she used to keep twisting me around until I was doing all sorts of things I hated, just to please her.'

His tone was full of disgust and Sarah instinctively rushed to offer mitigating circumstances. 'She is a good bit older than you, Ben. About four years.'

'Really?' He looked astonished for a moment but the grimness quickly returned. 'She's a liar, too. Can't stand liars. I remember the way she dismissed the whole thing when Tramp died. Couldn't trust her after that.'

He threw Sarah a look of sharp concern. 'I don't like the thought of you working under her, Sarah. Machiavelli had nothing on that woman. The sooner we get you your own boutique the better.'

Her own boutique . . . marriage to Ben . . . Sarah was jolted back to her own problems. While she was in complete sympathy with Ben where Frances Chatfield was concerned, she still couldn't marry him just to escape from her work situation. Yet she had said she would marry him! How was he going to react to her confession when she told him the complete truth?

'You know, Sarah,' he said in a soft, confidential tone, 'I'd got to the point where I thought I was hopeless at picking women. That's why I got Angela on to the job. But I feel really good with you. No nasty prickles down the spine at all.' And he smiled at her, an oddly touching smile of happy approval.

It was on the tip of her tongue to say that she felt comfortable with him too, but she caught the words back in time. She had to make her position clear to Ben. Right now. She couldn't let this misunderstanding go on any longer, but it was terribly difficult to find the right opening. He had been so nice to her, was still being nice to her, and the stark truth was . . . she liked his niceness. But that was no excuse for postponing the inevitable.

'Ben . . .' she began determinedly.

'Yes?' He flashed an encouraging smile at her.

Shame squeezed her heart. At least, Sarah thought it was shame. It had to be shame. What else could it be? She forced herself to go on. 'About what I said this morning . . .'

Ben chuckled. 'Never felt more relieved in my life. I told myself I was only dropping in to apologise to you for taking advantage of what Angela reckoned was emotional rebound, but the fact is, Sarah, I was really hoping Angela was wrong. I just couldn't let it go. Like I said last night . . . you and I are something else again.'

The pleasure in his voice sent ripples of warmth right down to her toes. Which reminded her of the way Ben had massaged them last night . . . and then kissed her. But she had been off balance last night, common sense insisted. Now, in the clear light of day, she couldn't possibly consider marrying Ben. Even his sister had told her he would make a terrible husband.

She tried again. 'Julian was making it very difficult this morning, Ben. When you came——'

'You suddenly saw the light,' Ben popped in cheerfully, then grinned at her. 'You don't have to explain, Sarah. The way we agreed on how a marriage should be . . . we're in absolute harmony about it. I guess I should thank Julian for reminding you of how compatible we are.'

'Well . . . er . . . I'm not too sure about that, Ben,' Sarah put in tentatively, having been floored once again.

Were they compatible? They certainly seemed to have a lot of attitudes in common, but she hardly

knew the man. She had only met him last night!
Events had moved so fast that she could hardly
keep up with them, but she had to make a stand
now. The problem was that everything she said got
twisted against her. Perhaps a more indirect
approach might help.

'What about the woman that Angela found for
you?'

'No trouble. We'll square that up at the first
opportunity.' He chuckled again. 'I sure am going
to enjoy seeing Angela's face when we arrive back
tomorrow and tell her we're getting married.'

There was no way out of it except to be brutally
blunt, Sarah decided, much as it pained her to
disappoint him. 'Ben, what I said about marrying
you this morning ... well, I was in a bind at the
time and ... er ... maybe I went too far ...'

'Not at all. Quite all right. Glad you did. Best way
to deal with that chap. Very positive,' Ben said
admiringly.

He certainly wasn't making it easy for her. Sarah
took a deep breath. 'Ben, I can't just marry you off
the cuff, so to speak. You must understand that ...'

'It's all right, Sarah,' he cut in quickly. 'You did
say there were conditions and that's fair enough.'

Conditions! Sarah grasped that concept as
though it was her last lifeline. 'That's right,' she
agreed. All she had to do was think up some
conditions that Ben would find unacceptable and

he would withdraw from the idea of marrying her.

'What are the conditons?' he asked.

'Well ... umm ...' Did she really want to put him off?

'Don't worry. I'm sure we can work them out to our mutual satisfaction.'

His confidence warned her that they would have to be pretty tough. 'I'm ... er ... I need to think about them.'

'Sure. Take as much time as you like,' Ben said kindly. 'We've got the whole weekend. You just tell me when you're ready.'

Sarah breathed a quiet sigh of relief. The weekend with her parents would surely produce the answers to the questions that had been bombarding her heart and mind. She would get a much more rounded view of Ben Haviland's personality and character, and maybe she would be able to sort out precisely how she felt about him and his proposal of marriage. And it wouldn't really be wasting his time even if she did end up rejecting him. After all, he could still go back to Angela's candidate.

Sarah gradually relaxed. She had the rest of today and tomorrow before she had to think of something, and something was bound to come up that would make Ben see they weren't suited. Meanwhile, his presence would surely help her through a difficult weekend. Her mother could hardly bemoan the loss of Julian when a larger-than-life Ben Haviland was at Sarah's side.

They left the city behind and Ben purred the Ferrari along the F2 Freeway towards the Great Western Highway. 'Great car, isn't it?' he remarked. 'I had one the last time I was in Italy and really enjoyed driving it.'

'It's a marvellous car,' Sarah agreed, but his comment about Italy started her thinking more about him. Always on the move, Angela had said, and he had just come back from the States. It was an expensive way to live. And this car bought on a credit card . . . 'How do you make all your money, Ben?' she asked curiously. 'I know you said selling ideas, but what kind of ideas?'

'Oh, things that strike me as handy, or fun, or more efficient. It's simple really. Take, for example, the ring pulls on cans of drink. Now that was a brilliant idea. Then there's the Cabbage Patch dolls. Very smart concept there, making dolls like real babies with adoption papers and everything. It's coming up with a convenience, or something with great market appeal. That's what sells.'

'And what's the latest thing you've come up with?'

He chuckled. 'The Cyli-Silo.'

'You mean that cylindrical puzzle thing that's driving everyone crazy?'

'Uh-huh. Thought of it while I was playing computer games. Kind of thing you can fiddle with on a bus or a train, and with enough fascinating challenge in it to hook anyone from schoolkids to bank managers.'

'That's fantastic, Ben,' Sarah said, somewhat awed by his ingenuity.

'Mmm. Trouble is, it took off even better than I thought it would, and that's why I've got the tax problem. Worth millions. Literally,' he moaned.

It suddenly struck Sarah that a lot of women would jump at the chance to marry a man such as Ben. Not only was he wealthy, but he was reasonably young and very attractive as well. That he was still a footloose bachelor could only be attributed to his wariness of being trapped into a relationship where he couldn't call his soul his own. There was no doubt that her main attraction for him was the fact that she had expressed the same wariness.

But while she might want the freedom of her own individuality, Sarah did not want the freedom of being left entirely alone while her husband skipped off around the world for months or years at a time. She wondered how Ben would react to the condition that they actually spend their life together. Sarah looked at him consideringly. He certainly appeared happy enough to spend this weekend with her, even though it meant sharing it with her parents.

They reached the outskirts of Katoomba, the commercial heart of the City of the Blue Mountains, and instead of keeping on the highway Ben took the scenic route that bypassed the business centre. 'Long time since I've been up here,' he remarked with a smile that appealed for her indulgence. 'I'd like to take in the view if you don't mind.'

'Good to miss out on the traffic,' Sarah nodded.

No matter how many times she had seen the popular tourist spots like Echo Point where the stony peaks of the Three Sisters formed a unique landmark, Sarah never failed to be enthralled by the grandeur of the Blue Mountains—mountains and valleys rolling on and on as far as the eye could see, all wrapped in the distinctive blue haze caused by the eucalyptus oil projected into the atmosphere from the massed growth of millions of eucalyptus trees.

At one of the more spectacular vantage points along the road, Ben pulled the Ferrari over to the verge and parked. 'This is as good a place as any,' he said, his eyes sparkling at Sarah as he reached over to the back seat for his suit jacket. He drew a small velvet bag from one of its pockets. 'I got a few rings on approval since I wasn't sure of your finger size. I hope one fits. And if you don't like diamonds we can change it for something else on Monday.'

While Sarah's mind staggered under the pressure of this new development, Ben unwrapped a magnificent diamond solitaire ring. She was too mesmerised by the size of the blue-white stone even to think of protesting when Ben took her left hand and slid the ring on to her third finger.

It stuck on her second knuckle. 'Too small,' Ben muttered, and slid it off again. 'Maybe the next one.'

Sarah finally pulled herself together enough to stop him from unwrapping another small fortune. 'Please don't, Ben. I can't accept it. Not when . . . when we haven't got things properly settled yet,' she added hastily. Her eyes lifted to his in anxious appeal. 'Mum and Dad will think it's too rushed anyway. It'll raise questions, Ben. Truly it will.'

He frowned. 'Didn't think of that.' He heaved a disappointed sigh. 'I guess the ring can wait until tomorrow. But, Sarah . . .' his eyes were suddenly questioning hers with a very warm appeal, 'Sarah, I can't put this off any longer.'

Sarah told herself it was relief that prompted her ready acceptance of his kiss, but she couldn't fool herself that it was relief that made her respond to it. Not in the way she did, because she forgot all about everything, and every bit of sense she had was cut off for the duration, swamped by a galloping range of sensations that aroused a compelling desire for more. And the odd part was, it was not a demanding assault on her mouth, more an invitation to explore together, except that it was Ben who initiated and she who followed his subtle escalation of sensual excitement.

It took her some time to focus her eyes on him when Ben finally drew away. Her breathing was decidedly ragged. Every nerve in her body seemed to be jangling with heightened awareness. Her lips quivered with the need for the seductive pressure to be renewed. In a daze she saw Ben give a slight shake of his head, heard him drag in a deep breath. Then he slumped back into his own seat, decisively separating himself from her. He picked up her hand and stared down at it for long tension-filled moments as his fingers stroked over hers. Again he shook his head.

'That's pretty strong medicine. Very strong,' he muttered, then turned to her with a rueful smile. 'You sure do give a man a shot in the heart, Sarah.'

An embarrassed little laugh broke out of her own sense of incredulity. 'You have quite a forceful aim yourself, Ben.'

The smile split into a delighted grin. 'Didn't I say we'd be good together? And it's got nothing to do with perfume, either. Just great chemistry. Great!' he repeated with relish.

He put her hand back on her knee, patted it indulgently, then switched on the powerful engine and eased the Ferrari back on to the road. For the twenty minutes or so that it took to get to Mount Victoria, Sarah's wits were in a hopeless muddle. She had never given much weight to chemistry. She had always believed that it was emotional involvement more than physical attraction that made a kiss special. But she wasn't emotionally involved with Ben Haviland. How could she be? There hadn't been enough time!

It was only when Ben asked for street directions that Sarah made a concentrated effort to pull herself together. The moment they arrived, explanations would have to flow thick and fast. She hadn't even telephoned her mother to say that Julian wasn't coming. She had meant to call from Central Railway before catching the train but ... well, Ben Haviland certainly presented a *fait accompli*, and his personality was strong enough to dim any other considerations.

The street was a narrow one, so she directed Ben to park in the driveway. He was out of the car before Sarah had undone her seat-belt, and held her door open for her to alight. Then he worked some mechanism to push the seat forward so that he could lift out her overnight bag. He was just straightening up when her mother came shooting out of the house to greet them.

'Sarah! My goodness! What a lovely car! And you must be Julian,' she added, beaming an indulgent welcome at Ben.

'I'm afraid he's . . .' Sarah began, only to be cut off by her father who had followed on his wife's heels.

'Sarah! At long last! It's about time you turned up to see us with your young man,' he chided good-humouredly. He thrust a hand out to Ben. 'Pleased to meet you.'

Ben cheerfully shook the offered hand, an affable grin on his face as he replied, 'Pleased to meet you too, Mr. Woodley. And you, Mrs Woodley. But I think I ought to tell you I'm not Julian.'

'Not . . .' Martha Woodley turned a bewildered look on her daughter.

'I was just going to tell you, Mum. This is Angela's brother, Ben Haviland. He's . . . er . . . just come home from overseas and is staying in the apartment with us at present. And I—I've broken my engagement to Julian.'

To Sarah's relief, Ben took it upon himself to continue the explanations. 'He wouldn't have made Sarah happy, Mrs Woodley. Not the sort of chap you'd want as a son-in-law at all. In fact last night I think he would have hit her if I hadn't been there to stop him and send him on his way.'

'Hit Sarah?' her mother said in shocked tones.

'I didn't think he could be a good type, Martha,' Jack Woodley observed critically. 'Not when he works for the taxation department.'

'The taxation department!' Ben's face reflected his own deep displeasure with that particular arm of government.

'One of the higher echelons, Sarah told us. Getting after people who have earned their money the hard way. Never did think it was much of a job.'

'Couldn't agree more,' Ben said with feeling. 'A man like that is capable of anything. And that was just how he was treating Sarah. Capable of anything!'

'Not strong on family, either,' Jack Woodley added, showing his discontent with his daughter's ex-fiancé. 'He should have come to meet us before this. Sarah was always making excuses for him. Didn't even ask me for Sarah's hand. Not that it's done much these days, but it's a discourtesy, you know,' he said to Ben.

'Ah . . .' said Ben, shooting Sarah a grateful look. He stepped over and put his arm around her shoulders. 'I'm glad you mentioned that, Mr Woodley, because I want to tell you here and now, that's the very reason I'm here. Sarah's still thinking about what she wants, but as far as I'm concerned, I'd marry your daughter tomorrow. I want you to know my intentions straight away because I sure would like you to approve of them.'

He gave Sarah's shoulders a possessive hug and his face beamed his pleasure at her parents. 'You've got a great girl here, and nothing would make me happier than to have her as my wife. Knew it as soon as I met her. Hit me like a bolt of lightning. I get all my best ideas that way so I knew I was right.'

'Well . . . well . . .'

Sarah watched her mother struggle for speech and felt a sharp sympathy for her predicament. Ben had a natural flair for taking away anyone's breath.

'Well, you'd better come inside, I've got lunch ready,' she finished weakly.

'Very welcome,' her father added, his initial surprise being overtaken by a definite air of approval.

'Just get some things out of the car first,' Ben said eagerly, giving Sarah a look of happy triumph before releasing her.

He handed her mother the largest box of chocolates Sarah had ever seen. 'Hope you've got a sweet tooth, Mrs Woodley,' he said with an appealing grin.

'My goodness!' She shook her head, just as Sarah had been shaking her head ever since she had met Ben.

He loaded her father up with the bottles of whisky, cognac and port, plus a bottle of French champagne. 'Something to have with dinner, or after it,' he suggested hopefully.

'Glenfiddich! Now there's a great drop of whisky,' her father observed with pleasure. 'I must say I admire your style, my boy.'

The issue of Julian was completely buried, Sarah noted in dazed bemusement as they finally made their way towards the house, and even before they were inside Ben was invited to call her parents Jack and Martha. Her father took Sarah's overnight bag, saying he would put it in her room, and offered to show Ben to his, clearly delighted at the prospect of having him stay with them. Sarah followed her mother into the kitchen to help with the serving of lunch.

'He's very nice, Sarah. Very nice,' she enthused.

And what could she say to that except agree? Sarah had the distinct impression that Ben Haviland was an unstoppable steam-roller, and the way things were going, some extremely nimble foot-work would be required if she was to get out of marrying him. On the other hand, would marriage to him be such a bad move after all? Sarah felt very, very confused.

CHAPTER FIVE

HE hadn't put a foot wrong. Not so much as a
toenail. If he had set out to woo her parents into
thinking he would make the perfect son-in-law he
couldn't have put on a more effective act. And yet it
hadn't appeared to be an act. Not once throughout
the whole afternoon and evening had Ben Haviland
said or done anything that could be perceived as
false or forced.

He had answered her parents' curiosity about
him over lunch with open good humour. They had
been as impressed as Sarah with his inventive ideas
and marketing success. Her father had triumphantly produced a Cyli-Silo, all worked out
through trial and error, and listened with fascina-
tion as Ben explained how he had had the idea.

When invited to potter round the garden, he
pottered quite happily, showing interest in all that
her parents showed him. Dinner had been a totally
relaxed family affair, and when the inevitable
question was asked if he played cards, Ben
delighted her parents by challenging them to select
any card game at all and he would give them a run
for their money. He partnered Sarah against her

parents at bridge with a boyish enthusiasm that kept them playing until midnight, and no one could have doubted that he had enjoyed himself immensely.

Sarah heaved another sigh, turned her pillow over, and tried to settle herself more comfortably, but she knew sleep was a million miles away. Her mind was far too active, endlessly revolving the events of the day, examining them from every angle, and getting more confused than ever over the character of the man who was now ocupying the bedroom on the other side of the wall.

She wondered if he was asleep or still lying awake, as conscious of her nearness as she was of his. The way he had looked at her as they had said goodnight ... it was just as well her parents had been present. It was just as well they were in her parents' home, because Sarah wasn't at all sure how she would handle it if Ben started making love to her.

His eyes had been making love to her ever since they had arrived here, continually reminding her of that kiss in the car. Every time he spoke to her, turned to her, over lunch, in the garden, at the dinner table, with every play of the cards, those warm, blue eyes kept dancing with the sure knowledge that it would be good between them. Better than good. Great!

Chemistry, he called it. Strong medicine. And

Sarah had to admit that it was getting stronger with every hour passed in Ben's company. But all the sex appeal in the world would not turn him into the kind of husband she wanted. It was all very well for Ben to be the congenial homebody for one weekend. It probably had a novelty value for a man who was virtually homeless. But for how long could he stick to such a home life? How long would he be happy in it?

In a burst of frustration with her thoughts, Sarah kicked off the blankets and rolled out of bed. She was never going to get to sleep at this rate. She headed for the kitchen. A cup of hot chocolate might help, and if she read one of her mother's magazines for a while . . . anything to get her mind off this treadmill of unanswerable questions.

There was plenty of milk in the refrigerator. Sarah took out one of the cartons, found the tin of Milo, spooned a generous amount of the chocolate-flavoured granules into a large mug, and mixed in the milk. She placed the mug in the microwave oven, set the timer for two minutes and pressed the start button. She watched the ovenplate on its first revolution with a satisfied sense of positive action, then turned away to replace the carton of milk in the refrigerator.

The sight of Ben standing in the kitchen doorway almost startled her into dropping it. He wore only a bath-towel fastened around his hips and his naked torso was every bit as impressively masculine as his clothed physique had suggested.

'Hi!' he said with a semi-apologetic grin. 'I'm glad it's you.'

'I couldn't get to sleep,' Sarah said in an attempt to drag his gaze back up to her face. She hadn't bothered to pack a dressing-gown and her silk nightie not only clung to every curve of her body, but its neckline sliced a deep cleavage almost to her waist. There were a couple of pretty modesty bows stretching across the valley between her breasts, but the way Ben was looking at them, he certainly didn't find them modest.

'I couldn't sleep either,' he echoed rather belatedly, his attention clearly concentrated on other matters as his gaze roved to the lower curves of hip and thigh.

Sarah was suddenly very conscious of the bright fluorescent kitchen light. How transparent was the silk with all those kilowatts beaming through it?

'That sure is a lovely nightie you've got on, Sarah,' Ben murmured appreciatively, then gave his own attire a rueful glance. 'I borrowed this towel from the bathroom. Always sleep in the nude myself. Hope you don't mind.'

Mind? Mind the precarious covering of the towel, or his sleeping naked? What would it be like to go to bed with him? The microwave pinged time-up, dragging her mind off a disturbing array of very physical thoughts.

'I was just making some hot chocolate,' she said with a fluttery wave at the oven. 'Would you like a mug?'

'Sounds good,' Ben nodded and moved forward. 'But don't you bother. Just find me another mug and I'll make it myself.'

'It's no bother,' she said hastily, anxious to keep some distance between them. Her arm swept out to click open the oven door. 'You have this one and I'll . . .'

'No, that's yours,' he insisted, and reached for the carton of milk she still held in her hand.

His fingers brushed over hers, her grip slipped and before either of them could save it, the carton dropped on to the floor, spilling milk around their feet. They both swooped down, their heads colliding in the confusion of the moment. Sarah reeled back. Ben clutched her shoulder to steady her, apologising profusely as he scooped the carton upright to prevent any more spillage. 'You sit down. I'll clean this up,' he instructed, blue eyes stabbing concern into hers.

'No. No, I'm all right,' she said somewhat breathlessly. His face was very close to hers and his hand had brushed over her breast to take a better lifting grip under her arm. She almost flung herself away from him, words spilling from her tongue in a wild grab for normality. 'Mum keeps her cleaning sponges under the sink. I'll . . . I'll get some to . . . for wiping up.'

'I'll help,' he said eagerly, standing with her, placing the carton on the bench and turning on the tap for her to wet the sponges.

He took one from her. Together they squeezed out the excess moisture and then squatted down to mop up the milk. Sarah concentrated hard on the floor but her eyes were irresistibly drawn by the sheer physical attraction of the man. But when she darted a glance up at his eyes it was to find them riveted on the jiggle of her breasts as she swept the sponge over the floor.

She fairly leapt up, ostensibly to rinse out her sponge. He was right behind her, shoulder to shoulder, reaching around her arm to hold his sponge under the tap, too. Neither of them said a word. They bent down again, swishing their sponges around the floor as if racing the clock. Sarah's pulse had gone completely haywire. Her heart was hammering against her chest as she straightened up again. The floor was clean. Clean enough, anyway. They rinsed the sponges and laid them on the sink to dry out.

Sarah waited for Ben to move away. He didn't. His fingers softly stroked the nape of her neck and trailed slowly down the curve of her spine. She shivered. She had to break away from him. Had to, her mind dictated frantically, but he was turning her towards him and her body was weak putty in his gentle hands.

He moved closer, his body swaying against hers, the rough texture of the towel rubbing an electric awareness of every pressure through the thin silk of her nightie. Sarah's mind was jammed by a flood of sensational signals. Only her hands obeyed the dictates of conscience as they plucked in weak protest at his shoulders, but she was unable to stop the gasping sigh of pleasure that stole from her throat as his lips met hers and roved over them. The hungry need inside her instinctively answered his, quickly escalating into a passionate desire for more and more satisfaction.

Only when his mouth left hers to mark out a sensual trail down her throat did Sarah catch her breath both mentally and physically. This had to stop now or there would be no stopping Ben at all. The towel was no hindrance to him. Nor was her flimsy nightie.

The words she tried to form were strangled into an inarticulate cry as his hand found her breast, his palm fanning the silk that moulded the soft, sensitive flesh, moving in a circular rhythm that barely touched her yet teased her nipple into excited prominence. Sarah closed her eyes in passive surrender to the mesmerising pleasure of it.

Then his hand moved further across, fingers tugging at the fragile bows that held her nightie together. Defensive alarms shrieked around Sarah's brain. He would have her completely naked in a minute. She forced the words out. 'Ben . . . no! Please don't!'

They were barely a croak but he heard them. The fingers stopped their gentle tug. A sigh whispered over his last kiss on her throat and he slowly lifted his head. 'You don't want me to?' he asked, a husky reluctance slurring the words. Then he saw the confusion of desire and shame in her eyes and his hand instantly lifted to her cheek in a tender gesture of reassurance. 'It's all right. I'm sorry I— er—got a bit carried away.'

'Yes,' she choked out, all too aware of how nearly she had got carried away herself. Her body was still reacting to his. Never had she been so aroused to such a peak of wanting.

Ben eased a little distance between them. His hands dropped to her hips as if he wanted to pull her after him, but he sucked in a sharp breath and took a step backwards. His gaze fell to the aroused peaks of her breasts, the slight contraction of her stomach as she too breathed in sharply. She spread a hand on his chest in an instinctive warding-off action, yet the heat of his skin invited more touching. It took all her will-power not to run her hand further.

'It's too soon!' she cried, more in conflict with herself than him. Only days ago she had been with

Julian. Her innate sense of morality was shocked at the wanton response Ben had so easily evoked.

'Wrong place,' Ben muttered. He dragged his gaze back up to hers. 'There is something special between us, Sarah. You feel it too.'

A hot flush spread right through her body, confirming the truth of Ben's assertion even as her mind wildly tried to deny it. 'Ben, I don't want— it's getting in too deep.' Her eyes clung to his in frantic appeal. 'I've hardly had a chance to ... to sort out what our relationship is.'

His face split into a grin of happy anticipation. 'Our relationship is that we're getting married. And it can't be soon enough for me.'

The reminder of her agreement jolted Sarah into an agitated escape from the disturbingly sexual attraction of the man. She paced the length of the kitchen, a turbulent jumble of thoughts storming through her mind. When she turned, Ben was still where she had left him, but his expression was now one of puzzled concern.

'But it's not a loving marriage, is it, Ben?' she shot at him testily. 'It's just a business arrangement that solves your tax problem, and if I go to bed with you, well, that's simply a convenient fringe benefit. Nothing more. And I ... I don't want to be used like that.'

'Used?' He picked up on the word as if it deeply offended him. 'Is that how you felt just then? That

I was using you?'

The accusation wasn't fair and Sarah knew it. 'I'm sorry.' She shook her head in helpless bewilderment. 'I shouldn't have responded like that. How can it be right? Only last week I was with Julian and . . .'

'Whatever you had with him has nothing to do with us, Sarah. Nothing!' Ben repeated emphatically. He moved, walking purposefully towards her.

Sarah put out an arm to ward him off. 'Please don't start again, Ben.'

He shook his head. 'I can see we've got some talking to do.' She flinched back as he lifted his hands but he gently caught her face and held it still. His eyes bored through the confusion in hers. 'Don't start putting nasty labels on what we just shared, Sarah. It was good. And I sure as hell don't think of making love to you as a fringe benefit. If we never married, I'd still want to hold you and kiss you and make love with you. Don't you feel the same way?'

'I . . . I need time to be sure,' she protested, even while she was inwardly fighting to stop herself from straining forward into another embrace. Whatever it was . . . the intimacy of the late hour, their state of undress, the immediacy of contact . . . it was all playing absolute havoc with her nerves. 'Please, could we sit down at the table and get a few things sorted out?' she asked, desperately needing a breathing space in order to think straight.

The hurt disappointment in his eyes stabbed her with guilt, yet what else could she have said or done? It was against her whole nature to plunge recklessly into a physical affair. She had never believed in casual sex and couldn't bring herself to accept it now, no matter how strong the temptation.

Reluctantly he let her go and pulled out one of the kitchen chairs for her. 'You sit down, Sarah. I'll bring you your drink.'

She had forgotten all about the mug of hot chocolate in the microwave. She felt so shaky it was a relief to sink on to the chair and let Ben serve her. He took his time, reheating her drink and making one for himself. To her further relief he offered her an apologetic smile as he took the chair opposite her.

'I didn't mean to rush you, Sarah. Fact is, I keep forgetting about your involvement with Julian. All I can think of is you and me, and that's a pretty big blind spot.'

Sarah was intensely grateful for his understanding, but she could not let him accept the blame for her own weakness. 'Maybe I've wanted to be blind too, but there are other considerations, Ben,' she started tentatively.

'I realise that. But I want you to know I won't

put any pressures on you, Sarah.' The blue eyes shot her a sharp look of anxiety. 'I wouldn't want to make you unhappy.'

He meant it, Sarah thought, deeply touched by the caring consideration he was showing her. She liked him very much—his openness, his kindness, his easy affability, the way he touched her, kissed her. She really did like him, and it was hard to say the words that had to be said, but she could not keep fooling herself and him any longer.

'Ben, you're not really planning on us living together, are you?' she said slowly. 'I mean, you'll be away a lot, overseas . . .'

He frowned at her, sensing a problem and wary of what it might mean. 'I've always enjoyed travelling but . . .' The frown cleared. 'I'd certainly like a permanent place here that I could return to. We'll buy a home for us, Sarah. Anywhere that'll suit you. I don't mind. I'd like that with you, Sarah. But you'd be free to come and go, just as you like. No prison, I promise you.'

Sarah's heart sank. In her fierce resentment of Julian's treatment of her, she had spouted those terms last night—was it only last night?—yet it wasn't what she wanted of a marriage. She wanted to share much more than a house, and on more than a part-time basis. She sighed and shook her head.

'It's not a house, Ben. I guess what it comes

down to is making a home and having a family, and
you see . . .' her eyes begged him to undertstand,
'. . . if I married you, we'd never have those things.
That's too high a penalty to pay, Ben, even for all
you would give me in other ways.'

He looked stunned. So stunned that Sarah was
doubly ashamed of having let him commit himself
so far before confessing what she now suddenly
recognised as her innermost needs. 'I'm sorry. I
had no right to say I'd marry you when I can't be
the kind of wife you want.'

His expression underwent a lightning change, an
urgency snapping into his eyes as his hands threw
out an appeal. 'But I do want you! I want you more
than any woman I've ever met. And who said we
couldn't have children? I'll admit I hadn't thought
that far ahead. Hadn't thought of having kids at all.
I guess I've been dumb and stupid as well as blind,
but that doesn't mean to say I wouldn't like them.'

Her resolution was momentarily shaken by the
unexpected concession from him, but the reason
behind it could not be overlooked. Ben wanted her,
but how long did desire last where there was no
commitment of love? 'Children don't fit into your
life-style, Ben,' she explained sadly. 'That's why
you haven't thought of them. And children need a
father who's there for them, not on the other side of
the world.'

For the first time he looked really troubled. 'I

think I'd be all right with kids, Sarah,' he said slowly. 'I'd probably have to go on business trips now and then, but I guess I could adjust to . . .'

'No.' The firm negative drew his anxious attention and she gave him a rueful smile. 'You see, Ben? I'm already putting pressure on you to change, to do something you don't want to do and be something you don't want to be. That's precisely the kind of marriage you're trying to avoid, and I don't blame you. I hated that kind of pressure myself. I don't want to do it to you. It wouldn't be fair.'

She pushed herself to her feet, suddenly very tired and a little sickened by all the mistakes she had made. 'I'm the wrong woman for you, Ben. You only need to solve a tax problem. You don't want to be burdened with a wife and children who'd want you to share your life with them. I'm sorry I've wasted your time.'

'Wait, Sarah!'

She had already reached the doorway and the scrape of his chair on the tiled floor sent a shiver down her spine. Her conscience was now clear and she didn't want to get muddled again. For a moment she swayed from pure fatigue, but the strong attraction of the man pulled her gaze back to him. She had to glance up because he was already at her shoulder. His eyes held an anxious tenderness as he lifted his hand to stroke her cheek in a soft salute.

'You haven't wasted my time, Sarah. I've enjoyed being with you and your family, and I'd like to ask for some more of your time.'

'Ben, I'm about ready to drop. What more is there to say?'

'Nothing right now,' he acknowledged and planted a soft kiss on her forehead. 'You go to bed. I want to think about what you've said. Maybe it's what I want, too. Just don't wipe me off yet, Sarah. Promise me that?'

The appeal lifted some of the leaden weight from her heart, but she felt driven to strip him of any false illusions. 'Ben, there'll always be other women you can make love with.'

'But will I ever forget what I might have had . . . with you?' he asked seriously.

'Sooner or later it'd be a prison for you. Don't forget that.'

He looked so disturbed, like a little boy who had just been slapped in the face with the hard realities of grown-up life. Sarah reached up and kissed his cheek on a wave of tender affection. 'Goodnight, Ben,' she murmured, then hurried off to her bedroom before he got any other ideas.

'Sarah . . .'

The hoarse roughness of the whispered call scraped over her heart. It seemed to express so much of what she was feeling herself, so much that had been so close, almost within reach, a promise that shimmered so enticingly, but a mirage nevertheless. She clutched at her door-jamb, needing its physical support as well as the reminder that life was full of doorways and some were better left closed. With a regret that was painfully intense, she looked back at the dark silhouette framed by the kitchen light. An arm was stretched out to her. It slowly fell.

'Goodnight, Sarah.'

The soft benediction had a ring of finality to it. She did not answer. She stepped inside her room and closed the door. Her eyes brimmed with tears as she laid her head despondently on her pillow. There had been something special between her and Ben, some deep affinity that had never been reached with Julian in all the months they had been together. As she drifted into sleep, her heart ached for what she might have had with Ben Haviland if Fate had shaped their goals in life to a matching end.

CHAPTER SIX

SARAH slept late. When she awoke she wished she had slept even later, or even, not woken up at all. There was nothing about this day she wanted to face. She winced at the thought of facing her parents' pleasure in Ben, and mentally shied away from the emotional strain of facing Ben himself. Tomorrow would begin another round of confrontation with Frances Chatfield's spite at the store. And then what was ahead of her? A big, fat zero! Sarah was not even sure she wanted to face up to the rest of her life.

But that was being unnecessarily defeatist, she told herself as she pushed herself out of bed. Who could tell what might turn up in the future? Hadn't Ben burst into her life like a bolt from the blue, shaking everything up? And at least she didn't have Julian to contend with any more. As incredible as it seemed, she no longer felt even the slightest twinge of regret for the loss of that relationship. And that undeniable fact brought a heavy frown of self-examination to Sarah's brow as she dressed.

She couldn't have loved Julian. There had certainly been a time when she had felt herself in love with him, and she had clung on to that notion in the teeth of one disillusionment after another until the last thread of emotional involvement had been bitten through. They had seemed so well suited to each other, enjoying the same kind of activities and finding a mutual satisfaction in the life-style they had planned for the future. Was that why she had clung so hard?

Perhaps she had it all wrong. Perhaps those things didn't matter as much as how well two people reacted together. On the surface, she and Ben weren't suited at all, yet . . . why did she feel so right with him? So right that she could never have been satisfied with the kind of psuedo-marriage he had proposed.

If she couldn't have his children . . . Sarah shook her head over the way that had slipped out last night and become one of the conditions of marrying him. It had surprised her even when she had said it. She simply did not know Ben Haviland well enough to say that she loved him. Or even well enough to fall in love with him. But she wished . . .

Sarah dragged her mind back from such futile thoughts and gave her hair a hard brushing. She carefully applied the complementary make-up to the casual fashion outfit she was wearing. Dark, plum-coloured slacks were topped by a loose-weave sweater that featured a daring design of plum-roses entwined with indistinct, sea-green foliage and wafts of dark mauve in the background. Sarah was pleased with the effect and felt satisfied that her appearance presented an air of being all together, even if she was a total mess inside.

She found her mother in the kitchen, preparing the usual Sunday roast dinner. 'Sorry I'm late up, Mum, but don't worry about breakfast. I'll just have a cup of coffee,' she said quickly in the hope of avoiding a fuss.

Martha Woodley sighed and shook her head. 'No wonder you're so thin.'

Sarah smiled at her mother's plump figure. 'Not thin, Mum. Just fashionably slim. Where is everyone?' she added casually.

'Your father's taken Ben for a stroll around the town. What there is of it,' she added, before lifting her eyes to her stubbornly single daughter. 'He's very nice, Sarah. He fits in so well, just like one of the family.'

'Yes,' Sarah agreed briefly, although the irony of her mother's statement was not lost on her. If Ben was really a family man he wouldn't be the 'maverick' he was. Angela probably knew him better than anyone, and she certainly didn't believe that the leopard could change his spots.

Martha Woodley was not content to let the matter drop. Ben's virtues were pointed out in a steady stream of observations to ensure that her daughter had a full appreciation of them. To Sarah's relief, her mother did refrain from actually suggesting an acceptance of Ben's proposal, but the message was loud and clear.

Sarah did not feel inclined to disillusion her mother over the type of husband Ben would be, so she kept her replies short and non-committal. As it was, she found the conversation depressing and was almost glad when her father and Ben returned. Until her eyes met Ben's and every nerve in her body knotted with tension.

He still wanted her. And she wanted him. Their conflict over the marriage issue had not diminished the desire that had leapt between them last night. If anything, it was now heightened by the short time that was left to them . . . if Sarah did not weaken from the stance she had taken. And she couldn't. She had thought it all through. She had to stand firm and let Ben go his own way or they would both be miserable.

Sarah did not know how she got through the next couple of hours. Her whole body vibrated with an electric awareness every time Ben came near her, so much so that if he touched her she flinched. Her mind could not concentrate on any line of conversation for long and she noted that Ben was similarly distracted. Fortunately her parents had a lot to say and did not remark on their lapses.

She ate the meal her mother served but she could not remember tasting any of it. She dropped one of the plates in the kitchen when clearing up, and when Ben stooped with her to pick up the pieces, she literally started to tremble with the force of her emotional turmoil. A sharp edge of broken crockery nicked her finger and she used the minor wound as an excuse to flee to the bathroom, desperate to regain some composure.

Her parents always went to their bowling club on Sunday afternoons so she and Ben were expected to take their leave straight after lunch. For Sarah it could not be soon enough. She had to say goodbye to Ben as quickly and as cleanly as possible, and even the journey down the mountain in the intimacy of the Ferrari promised to be pure torment. There was no future in any relationship between them. She had to keep remembering that.

Having steeled herself to remain calm and in control, Sarah managed to act quite normally as her parents accompanied her and Ben to the car. She kissed them goodbye and said all that was expected of her. Then Ben completely threw her by handing her the car keys.

'You drive, Sarah.'

She looked up at him in startled surprise. Julian had never allowed her behind the wheel of the Alfa, and here was Ben inviting her to drive his Ferrari!

'You would like to, wouldn't you?' he pressed, seeing her uncertainty. 'Most people would, at least once in a lifetime.'

Once in a lifetime ... Of course! Ben had prmised not to pressure her and he knew as well as she did that this afternoon was all that was left to them. And he was right. She would like to drive a car like this and she would probably never have another chance. She nodded, too distressed to speak. He took her arm to steer her round to the driver's side of the Ferrari and this time she didn't flinch at his touch. She welcomed it, wanted it, wished there could be more.

Her mother's shocked voice broke the intimacy of the moment. 'But the car's too valuable, Ben. You can't let Sarah ...'

'Don't tell me you think men drivers are better than women, Martha,' Ben tossed at her teasingly. 'It's a well known fact that women are more safety-conscious on the road. Besides, I'd probably fall asleep at the wheel after stuffing myself on that great dinner you just cooked.'

'Ben, are you sure?' Sarah asked anxiously as he opened the door for her.

The look he gave her sent a shivery feeling right down her spine. 'I'd be happy for you to drive me anywhere, Sarah. Anywhere at all.'

She had no answer to that. She was much too aware that he was referring to a lot more than driving a car, even a Ferrari. She settled rather nervously into the seat and Ben closed the door on her. Her eyes literally ached as she watched him shake hands with her father and heard both her parents say he would be welcome again at any time. They meant it in all sincerity, and somehow that twisted the knife even further. There was no hope that such a visit would ever be repeated.

As Ben climbed in beside her she wondered how

much having children really meant to her. After all, if she never married she would never have them. But to marry someone where children would be an impediment to their life-style . . . No, she couldn't do it. She would want them. She knew she would, sooner or later, and that wouldn't be fair to the children.

She barely heard Ben's instructions as he explained the basic instruments. His hand had covered hers to take her through the necessary gear changes and a tingling warmth was racing through her veins. She switched on the engine when he told her to and only when she had activated the correct gear did his hand leave hers, fingers trailing softly over her slender wrist before falling away. She concentrated so fiercely on handling the powerful car that she forgot to wave to her parents.

Not that it mattered. They would understand, she assured herself. Driving a Ferrari was a daunting as well as an exciting experience, and it also served to force her attention off Ben. It was bad enough that she could feel him watching her, but she knew it would have been far worse sitting in the passenger seat watching him. She kept her eyes firmly fixed on the road. They had been travelling for some ten minutes before Ben broke the silence between them.

'Relax, Sarah,' he said softly. 'The car won't buck if you hold the wheel less tightly.'

Only then did she notice her clenched grip. It

took a conscious effort to unclench her fingers and, try as she might, she could not fully relax. 'It's . . . it's just getting used to the feel of it,' she excused herself.

'I like the sweater you're wearing,' he suddenly commented, making her even more aware of his continual appraisal.

'It's a Penny Walker,' she said out of the sheer necessity of saying something, anything to inject some normality into the atmosphere of the car.

'Is that some special trade name?'

Sarah snatched at the remark as if it were a lifeline. 'Not yet, but it will be. Penny Walker is a brilliant young designer who's looking for a fashion outlet for her clothes. I was in the middle of persuading the store management to take up a contract with her when Julian pulled his act last Friday.' The bitter memory of defeat put a sharp edge on her tone of disgust. 'Our mutual friend, Frances Chatfield, spiked the whole deal while I was out of the conference room. That woman is so rigidly narrow-minded she simply refuses to acknowledge that any other view could be better than her own. To her, fashion is understated elegance, preferably in neutral or earth colours. The safe things,' Sarah added in scornful contempt.

'Like a steady job,' Ben said in sympathetic understanding.

'Exactly. There's no room in her mind for new

ideas, particularly anything that's totally noncon-
formist. And she's full of jealous spite for anybody
who excels her. She's so terribly wrong about
Penny Walker's designs. Stupidly, blindly wrong!
The young market is crying out for bright,
dramatic clothes that are fun to wear, colours and
combinations that make the wearer feel positive
and individual. In my opinion, Penny Walker will
go to the top once she breaks into the market. She's
so marvellously innovative.'

'Sounds like my kind of person,' Ben said
approvingly.

'Mine too,' Sarah agreed with feeling.

The words echoed in her mind, over and over
again in the silence that followed. They magnified
the strong affinity that leapt so naturally between
her and Ben whenever they talked ... even when
they didn't talk. The sense of closeness—of mutual
understanding and desires and needs—was almost
overwhelming in the intimate confinement of the
car.

She couldn't let him go, Sarah thought with
sinking desperation. She couldn't bear to send him
away to marry someone else. She had to hold on.
But how could she do that when Ben hated to be
pinned down?

'Do you like dogs, Sarah?'

The quiet question took some time to penetrate
her emotional turmoil. She answered distractedly.
'We had a marvellous dog when we were kids.

Honey. That was her name. She was a Labrador. We all adored her. Even Mum, though Honey used to dig up her garden sometimes.' Sarah suddenly remembered the dog that Frances Chatfield had poisoned. 'Was yours a Labrador?'

'No. Tramp was a Border collie.'

'That must have been awful ... losing him like that. We were terribly sad when Honey died, but at least she'd lived a full and very happy life.'

'Yes. A full life,' Ben murmured.

And there was the catch, Sarah thought despairingly. How could she live a full life with Ben when ...?

'Sarah ...'

Ben's hand slid warmly over her thigh. Every nerve in her body went haywire. She couldn't prevent herself from jerking the wheel in desperate reaction to his touch. The Ferrari went off the road and headed for two solid gum trees before Sarah's vision cleared enough to realise the car had bolted on her. Sheer terror gripped her heart. They were going to crash! She found her foot jammed hard on the accelerator and instantly transferred it to the brake but there was no time to stop. The trees were rushing at them, the car bucking over the rough underbrush as if eager to hurl itself to destruction.

Panic screamed through her head that they were going to die. The grim need to survive billowed over it, insisting that she had to keep her head ... control whatever she could as long as she could.

Somehow she steered a safe passage between the trees but despite a desperate swing of the wheel she side-whacked another just beyond them. The car slewed around, collided with something else, flinging Sarah sideways and then into oblivion.

Ben's voice came spiralling through dark, dizzying pain, forcing an awareness of something, something bad and frightening. Her mind moved sluggishly towards it.

'Sarah! Oh God! Sarah, please wake up. Please!'

She forced her eyes open, needing to see, to know. Ben's face swam in front of her.

'Wass th' matter?' Her voice came out slurred, furry.

Ben heaved a sigh and muttered several vehement words under his breath, all of them unintelligible to her. He was dabbing something at her left temple and it hurt. She lifted a hand to stop him.

'It's OK, Sarah,' he soothed. 'Just a small scalp wound but it's bleeding rather a lot. Can you move your legs?' he asked anxiously.

Legs, she repeated in her mind until the message filtered through the fog and stirred her feet.

'Good girl!'

She heard the deep relief in Ben's voice but didn't understand it. Why was he worried about her legs? It was her head that hurt. She must have hit it on something. Then with a lightning burst of clarity she remembered. The car! She had crashed Ben's Ferrari!

Her eyes opened wide, their focus sharpening on the shattered windscreen that had been pushed outwards. She turned her head and found Ben crouched at the opened door on her side. 'How bad is it?' she cried, her feet already scrambling to get out.

'Don't worry about it,' Ben advised quickly. 'I think you'd better stay sitting down.'

'No! No! Let me out! I'm all right!' she insisted wildly, a rush of guilt driving her to examine the damage.

She virtually threw herself out of the car, defying Ben's protests, and suddenly found she wasn't all right at all. Her head performed dizzying circles and she could not have kept upright but for Ben's strong support. His arms came around her in a steadying embrace and she leaned against him until the world stopped spinning.

'It's only a car, Sarah,' he said gruffly. 'For God's sake! Let me look after you.'

'I'm fine,' she lied, resting her head on his shoulder and feeling a lot more alive as the warmth of his body soaked into hers.

Very slowly and carefully she turned her head so that her gaze could take in the car, and then she stared at it in incredulous horror. The whole chassis was bent into a banana shape. Deeply scored scratches disfigured the gleaming bonnet. The back tyre was flat and misshapen. There was not the remotest possibility that this poor twisted wreck of a car would be driven anywhere. She had just written off a Ferrari!

'Oh, my God!' she gasped, absolutely stricken by the enormity of what she had done.

'Don't worry about it. It's insured. It's no problem to get another car,' Ben insisted.

Her eyes sought his, her own guilt stirring anger at his seemingly careless attitude. 'You shouldn't have touched me like that!'

'I know. I didn't stop to think what I was doing,' he admitted gravely.

'It was irresponsible and ... and ...'

'Completely my fault.'

'I was so uptight about ...'

'I know. Me, too. I couldn't stand it any longer. I had to touch you. Couldn't help myself.'

'Oh, Ben ...'

It was a cry of protest against her own ravening need for him and the force of it shook her weakened system even more. There was no fight left in her, no resistance. She slumped against him and his arms enfolded her in a comforting blanket of warm security.

Sarah was barely aware of time passing, of people milling around them, of voices asking questions. She vaguely heard Ben talking. The thought drifted through her mind that maybe she should stir herself to do or say something but her head was feeling woozy again and it was easier just to let Ben be in command.

The next thing she knew someone was tucking a blanket around her and she was lying down somewhere. She cried out in alarm and a gentle hand stroked her cheek. 'Everything's fine,' Ben assured her. 'We're in an ambulance and we're taking you to the hospital at Penrith for treatment. You got a nasty knock on the head, Sarah.'

'Did I black out again?' she asked anxiously.

He nodded. 'Probably concussion. And shock.' He took her hand and gently fondled it. 'Don't worry about a thing. I'll look after you.'

Tears welled into her eyes. 'I'm sorry about the car, Ben. You shouldn't have let me drive.'

'Nonsense! You're a great driver.' He suddenly grinned at her. 'The way you slid us between those trees ... like threading a needle. Stirling Moss would have been proud of you.'

It won a watery smile from her.

'That's better. I like it when you smile,' he said huskily.

'Ben, will you stay with me? At the hospital?'

'They'd have to use crowbars to pry me from your side.'

'Thank you,' she whispered in heartfelt relief. The thought of being left alone in a big, impersonal hospital was rather frightening. Especially if there was something really wrong with her head, like a fractured skull.

Ben was as good as his word, staunchly refusing to accept the suggestion by various medical personnel that Sarah be left in their care. Even while a doctor examined her eyes and when she was wheeled up to the X-ray department Ben remained at her side. It was an enormous relief when she was pronounced clear of all injury except mild concussion and a slight cut above her left temple. However, the recommendation was that she stay in hospital for a couple of days and Ben wouldn't hear of her disobeying this edict.

'But I've got to go to work tomorrow,' Sarah protested.

'Your health and well-being are more important,' he insisted. 'You'll probably be as weak as water tomorrow. Shock does that to you. I'll get Angela to ring up the store and explain your absence. Angela's very good at fixing things like that.'

Fixing other things too, Sarah thought despondently, like getting a suitable marriage candidate who would leave Ben free to live as he liked. He was holding her hand again. In fact, he had barely let it go throughout all the business at the hospital, and Sarah had taken a great deal of comfort from that steady, silent support. She stared down at the strong fingers enfolding hers, secretly wishing that the link did not have to be broken. It was such a good feeling, having Ben look after her.

'I'm sorry I've been so much trouble to you,' she sighed, knowing that their parting had only been postponed by the accident, and tomorrow would bring a return to the inevitable.

'Sarah . . .'

Reluctantly she dragged her gaze up to his, hoping that he would not see how disturbed she felt at the thought of tomorrow, and all the other tomorrows without him at her side. His eyes searched hers with an urgent intensity that made her heart flutter.

'How many kids would you like to have, Sarah? What I mean is, well, if we're going to have a family, I reckon we ought to have a few, don't you?'

Her heart did more than flutter. It catapulted around her chest. 'You—you want a family?' she choked out.

His mouth curved into a funny little smile. 'I hadn't really considered it until you brought it up last night, but I figure you're right. It's like you said in the car before we crashed, about your dog, Honey, having lived a full life. I suddenly realised that I've been more or less skating over the surface, not touching down anywhere long enough to make any meaningful mark. Then when that tree was looking me in the face I thought, this is it! Your number's up! And you've damned little to show for your thirty-four years.'

Uncertainty shadowed the hope that had sprung into Sarah's mind. 'But to have children just for the sake of leaving behind an extension of yourself . . .'

'Hell, Sarah, I don't have that big an ego! No, I

mean to do the thing right. Be a proper dad to them, like your father. He was telling me all about it this morning.'

'You'd stay at home and not keep travelling?' She still couldn't quite believe he meant it.

He grinned. 'We could make a real home, Sarah. Have a big garden so we could have a couple of dogs for the kids. No reason why a Labrador can't get along with a Border Collie if we get them as pups together.'

He spoke with such eager enthusiasm that Sarah couldn't doubt his sincerity. Right at this moment he did want the family-life future he was picturing, but it was the accident that had really triggered his decision. A brush with death often prompted people into an impulsive resolution to change their ways. When it actually came to living the shiny new life, old habits died very hard.

'And you can still run your boutique because I'll be at home to mind the kids,' Ben concluded with an air of having worked everything out very satisfactorily.

Sarah could not accept that he would be satisfied in the long run. 'But what would you do, Ben?'

'When you're inventing things, it doesn't matter where you are, Sarah. I like fooling around on computers so I'll get a couple to play with. I never have any trouble amusing myself.' The grin came again, sparkling with pure pleasure. 'And then there's the best thing of all . . .'

'What's that?'

'I'll be married to you.'

And that was at the heart of it all, Sarah reminded herself. He needed to get married and he wanted her.

His grin faded at her lack of response and his brow puckered with concern. 'Are there any other conditions, Sarah?'

She shook her head and a warm tenderness filled her eyes as she looked at the man who would give her everything she wanted ... at this moment in time. 'I'd love that, Ben. To have the kind of life with you that you described just now. But I can't help feeling that you might regret rushing into such a big commitment. It's not what you wanted before this weekend and ...'

'That's because I needed you to enlighten me,' he said with beaming confidence.

It was too much for Sarah to fight. She wanted to give in, to believe it could all come true. Only a persistent nagging of common sense urged one necessary caution. 'Let's wait a few days, Ben. You might have second thoughts about it all. What with the accident and everything else——' her eyes probed his anxiously '—there've been too many pressures, Ben.'

'If that's what you want,' he agreed reluctantly. 'But I'm not going to change my mind and talking about pressures——' a deeper warmth kindled in his eyes '—Sarah, I know this isn't exactly the best place, but I've been wanting to kiss you all day.'

'Me, too,' she breathed.

And it was quite some time before she breathed again.

When Ben was finally ordered from the hospital room by the night nurse, Sarah felt more confused than ever. Neither she nor Ben had spoken of love, but the way Ben made her feel . . . Sarah was no longer sure of what love was, anyway. She knew in her head that if they married it would be a terrible gamble, but her heart was hopelessly set on taking that gamble—if Ben didn't change his mind.

Maybe tomorrrow he would have second thoughts. Or the next day. Or the next. When he really stopped to think of the restrictions that would be placed on his free-roving spirit, would he take fright and run? It worried Sarah. It worried her more than she liked to admit, but there was nothing she could do but wait and see. And hope.

CHAPTER SEVEN

'SARAH?'

A wave of relief rippled through her at the sound of Ben's voice. She gripped the telephone receiver more tightly, as if the extra pressure could bring him closer to her. The morning in the hospital had seemed endless. She had been woken at six o'clock and from that early hour she had been waiting and hoping for some contact from Ben, wanting reassurance that he was still happy about his proposal.

'Yes, it's me,' she breathed happily. 'And the doctor's checked me over and I'm fine, except for being a bit shaky. How are you?'

'Relieved to hear you're OK. Has a policeman been around to interview you about the accident, Sarah?'

'No.'

'Good! If one turns up, say you don't remember what happened. That's fair enough with concussion. I'll get you off any charge, Sarah. I'll say the tyre had a blow-out and the car ran off the road.'

'But . . . that's a lie.'

'Mmm. There's not much justice in you being

put through a stupid court case. No one else's car was involved and you were the only one hurt. Please, just say you don't remember what happened, Sarah, and leave the rest to me. It was all my fault, anyway, and I don't want you to be further distressed by it.'

Did he really feel the accident was his fault? In the eyes of the law it might not be, and Sarah squirmed at the thought of a truthful report being read out in court. 'All right, Ben. I'll do as you advise,' she said quickly.

'That's a load off my mind. Now, Sarah,' his tone became briskly purposeful, 'I've got a lot of people to see today so I don't know when I'll get back to you. Maybe not until tonight. Is there anything you need?'

'A fresh change of clothes. If you ask Angela . . .'

'Right! No problem. Anything else?'

"No, I don't think so.'

'How's your head? Still aching?'

'No. They keep giving me pills.'

'Good! Keep taking them. Got to fly now, Sarah. 'Bye.'

She felt deflated by the brief, matter-of-fact conversation. Ben wasn't coming to see her until tonight and he hadn't even told he what he was doing. Only slowly did Sarah's common sense rally over her disappointment. Of course Ben would be busy today. He wasn't running out on her. He had

to see about the car and ... and the insurance ...
and ... whatever. There was no need to torment
herself with doubts just because he had seemed
rather brusque on the telephone. Some people
weren't comfortable with telephone conversations.

Nevertheless she felt a lot better when an hour or
so later a hospital aide came in with a lovely basket
of flowers. 'Penny Walker special', Ben had written
on the card, and Sarah laughed with pleasure on
noticing the vibrant colour contrasts of the flower
arrangement. She firmly put aside all her misgiv-
ings about Ben's flightiness. They had something
special going between them, as Ben put it, and the
flowers were a beautiful reminder of how closely
they were attuned to each other.

No policeman came, much to Sarah's relief, but
it was a long day, with nothing for her to do except
think, and the fact that she and Ben had only
known each other for such a short time continued
to prey on her mind. She wanted him with her,
needed him with her, and the evening visiting
hours would not come fast enough.

However, it was Angela who walked into Sarah's
room at seven o'clock, not Ben, and Sarah found
herself feeling oddly embarrassed at her friend's
frank scrutiny.

'Your clothes,' Angela said without any preamble, and placed a plastic carrier bag beside her bed.

'Thanks, Angela. It's very good of you to bring

them. I thought Ben——'

'He's off doing something else. I don't know what mischief he's up to and he won't tell me,' came the slightly acid comment as Angela settled herself on the bedside chair and frowned at Sarah. 'You certainly look all right. I've been wondering all day if that knock on your head has scrambled your brains. Do you feel your mind is clear, Sarah?' she asked doubtfully.

A self-conscious little laugh bubbled out of Sarah's throat. 'I guess it must seem pretty mad to you, taking Ben home with me after what I said on Friday night, crashing his Ferrari ...'

'I can understand the first part because Julian came to the apartment yesterday and told me what happened at the store.'

'Julian came to the apartment?' Sarah was amazed. She hadn't believed that Julian cared about her so much that he would put himself through another confrontation after the knock she had given him on Saturday. Did he care? Or was the blow to his ego smarting too much for him to put it aside? Sarah smothered a twinge of guilt. Julian had got what he deserved for behaving as he did at the store. And towards her!

'What I don't understand ...' Angela began again with arch emphasis, '... is why Ben has this unshakeable belief that you're going to marry him.'

Unshakeable. A smile grew inside Sarah and

danced into her eyes even before it curved her mouth.

'You're not, are you?' Angela demanded incredulously.

'I'm thinking about it, but not the kind of marriage Ben discussed with you, Angela,' Sarah hastily explained.

Angela stared at her, speechless, then shook her head as if nothing made any sense to her.

'He says he wants to have a family,' Sarah pleaded, wanting her friend to understand. 'A real marriage, not a financial deal, Angela. I know it's all terribly sudden, and I've told him we must have more time to be sure it's what we want, but ...'

'He'll never do it and you're mad to believe it, Sarah,' Angela said with utter certainty. 'He was going to have a real marriage once before and he ran out on it at the last minute.'

'Ben told me about that. He had a good reason, Angela,' Sarah said with equal certainty. 'This is different. We ... we understand each other,' she finished limply, since she felt rather self-conscious about confessing her precise feelings about Ben.

'Sarah, I don't think you understand a thing about my brother,' Angela said with weary scepticism. 'Just because he was on the spot to support you when you had a fight with Julian, that doesn't mean he'll stick around to support you for the rest of your life. You simply can't rely on him to act like any normal human being. Look what he did to me this weekend!'

She threw up her hands in exasperation. 'He shot off with you and didn't even bother to let me know what he was up to, or where he was. Which is typical! He just comes and goes as the fancy takes him. I had to put off the meeting I'd set up for him with the woman I'd found, and do some fast talking with her in case Ben changed his mind again.'

'What do you mean, changed his mind again?'

Angela heaved a sigh. 'Well, he told me before he left on Saturday morning that he didn't want anyone else but you, but after what you'd said to me on Friday night, I figured I'd better keep his options open.'

'Well, it wasn't Ben's fault that you decided to second-guess him,' Sarah argued staunchly.

Angela stared at her again, more speculatively this time, and a tide of warmth crept up Sarah's throat and spread into her cheeks. 'I told you it wasn't the money,' she said defensively.

'What's been going on since I saw you last?' Angela demanded to know.

Sarah hesitated for a moment, wondering if it was even possible to explain the subtle and not so subtle shifts of emotion that had taken place in the last three days. But it was clear that she had to try, or Angela would never be in sympathy with the situation. She sucked in a deep breath and plunged into confiding as much as she could to her friend.

Angela looked absolutely dumbfounded by the time Sarah had finished stating her case. 'Well, all I can say is God help you, Sarah, if you've fallen in love with Ben,' she finally commented. 'He's sure to break your heart if you take him on as a husband.'

'I didn't say I'd fallen in love with him. I said——'

'Classic case,' Angela declared gloomily. 'And here I've gone and put my foot in it with Julian.'

'What do you mean, put your foot in it?'

Angela sighed and shrugged as if she was carrying the burdens of the world. 'He seemed genuinely upset over losing you, and when he actually admitted that he had behaved badly, I thought perhaps he was seeing the light and might be prepared to change his ways for you.' Her hands lifted and fell in a helpless gesture. 'So I explained that Ben was my brother whom you'd only just met on Friday night and there was nothing serious between you.'

Sarah grimaced. 'So more than likely Julian will be coming after me again!'

Angela rolled her eyes. 'And he's not going to believe you're attached to Ben. I'm afraid I torpedoed that idea. Julian wanted to know why Ben had gone along with your claim that you were marrying him so I . . .'

'You didn't tell him!' Sarah cried in horror. 'You know Julian works for the taxation department!'

Angela frowned. 'It's not illegal to have a tax-deductible wife.'

'Oh, God!' Sarah groaned. 'It'd be just like Julian to go after Ben and try to make something of it once I tell him I don't want a reconciliation. I've heard him gloat over the way his investigators can get people's finances tied up in legal knots for years. If he does that to Ben because of me——'

Despair gripped her heart. Ben had spelt it out to her, how he hated pressures and being pinned down. It was questionable enough that she had pinned him down with children, but to have him pressured by tax investigators . . . It simply wasn't fair to put him through that.

'I can't do it,' she moaned.

'Can't do what?' Angela asked, clearly perturbed by her *faux pas* in saying too much to Julian.

'I can't marry Ben. I'd cause him too much trouble.'

Angela looked even more perturbed. 'Seems like I'm the one causing the trouble,' she muttered in self-disgust.

Sarah heaved a despondent sigh. 'Don't worry about it, Angela. You could be right about our marriage failing, anyway. Ben's probably acting on impulse because he wants me, and I . . .' she took a deep, painful breath, 'I guess I've just been dreaming.'

Angela frowned. 'I don't know, Sarah. Maybe you're the kind of woman Ben could be happy with. He was certainly happy last night. I thought his elation had to do with having persuaded you to marry him, but it could have been more than that.' She shrugged. 'I've been setting myself up as a judge and——'

The shrill ring of the telphone on top of the bedside locker startled both of them out of their joyless introspection. Sarah's heart fluttered in anxious hope as she picked up the receiver. Surely it had to be Ben, but why was he ringing? He had said he would come!

'Sarah?'

There was a note of anxiety in Ben's voice that added to her own. 'Yes, Ben,' she said quickly.

'Did Angela bring the things you wanted?'

'Yes. She's here now.'

'Ah! That's good. Nothing more miserable than being in hospital without a visitor. I can't make it tonight, Sarah, but I'll be there tomorrow to tell you all about it.'

'All right,' she said, but it didn't feel all right. Disappointment was flooding through her. 'Thanks for the flowers, Ben,' she added flatly.

'I had expert advice on those. Are you feeling better, Sarah?'

'Yes.' She tried to inject some lightness into her voice. 'I feel like a fraud for taking up a hospital bed.'

'Do whatever the doctors tell you. They know best. I'll see you tomorrow morning for sure. OK?'

'Yes, of course. Goodnight, Ben.'

There was a slight pause, then a sigh. 'Goodnight, Sarah.'

She put the telephone down, wondering if he was remembering how hungrily they had kissed the night before. Whether he felt the same desire now . . . as she did. But he hadn't come, she reminded herself despondently, and if they stayed away from each other . . .

'He's not coming to visit you, is he?' Angela commented cuttingly.

'Tomorrow, he said,' Sarah answered, unable to keep the disappointment out of her voice.

'I tell you, Sarah, you can't count on Ben. He's unreliable. He only thinks about what he wants to do. You'll be better off not marrying him.'

Sarah noted the ring of self-justification in Angela's tone but she could not ignore the fact that Ben's sister had a lifetime of knowing him. 'You're probably right,' she muttered.

There was an uncomfortable silence while they both contemplated the situation, then Sarah couldn't bear her friend's company any longer. 'Angela, if you don't mind, I'm—I'm rather tired.'

'I'll go.' Angela stood up abruptly but she hesitated, her expression clouded with uncertainty. 'I'm sorry I ever opened my mouth. About anything. I'll keep right out of your affairs from now on, Sarah. I promise.'

Sarah forced a smile. 'I know you meant well, Angela. Thanks for coming and bringing my stuff.'

Angela's smile was a twist of self-mockery. 'The good Samaritan who needs her tongue cut out. With my experience of crime reporting I should know better.'

'You did what you thought was best,' Sarah said in exoneration.

'That's what they say about murdered do-gooders,' Angela wisecracked on her way out the door.

But she had done some good, Sarah eventually acknowledged as she reviewed the events of the last few days. Angela had forced her into looking at the situation from a more objective perspective, and the longer Sarah considered her position, the more unreal and untenable it became.

Too much had happened too quickly. She wasn't sure where she was. Ben hadn't come to see her and had given no explanation for his absence. Angela was probably right. He was feckless and capricious, acting on impulse without any continuity of purpose. And Sarah suddenly realised that she was relying on him. She still felt hurt and disappointed that he hadn't turned up to be with her. Hadn't she learnt the lesson with Julian that the only person she could rely on was herself?

As for Julian, well, at least she had *that* problem sorted out as far as she was concerned. She didn't love him or want him. But he could become a very real thorn in Ben's side if he thought Sarah was marrying Angela's brother just for the money she would save him. If Julian kept up his pursuit of her she would have to make a very firm stand about her marriage to Ben.

The problem was, Sarah was no longer sure what that stand would be. She had never felt so compellingly attracted to a man, and it wasn't just physical. She liked everything about Ben: the way he talked to her and listened, his kindness and consideration of her feelings, his respect for her ideas and aims in life. But maybe that manner came easily to him because he hadn't had to sustain it for long. A weekend was hardly any test.

If he truly was as unreliable as Angela claimed, then he would show his true colours soon enough. After all, she didn't have to marry him. The taxation problem was Ben's, not hers. She had told him she needed time. It was his decision to stay with her rather than pursue a more certain course of resolving his problem. She wouldn't try to hold him if he wanted to back off from the marriage concept of family life. She wasn't at all sure he wasn't already backing off. Obviously they both needed time to be sure that they weren't making a terrible mistake.

Meanwhile she had to get her life back into order and that centred on her job. She had to get back to work tomorrow. It wasn't as if she were really sick, and God knew what Frances Chatfield might get up to if she stayed away any longer. After the scene on Saturday morning, Sarah had no doubt that Frances would do her spiteful best to undermine her authority in the Young Trends department even further.

Having settled on these decisive courses of action, Sarah slept quite well that night, but the next morning she ran into an unexpected difficulty. The day sister informed her that she could not leave the hospital until a doctor signed her out.

'But you can't keep me a prisoner here,' Sarah protested.

'If you go without the proper authority, the police will bring you back,' the sister stated, as immovable as a brick wall on rules and regulations.

'But I'm not sick. The doctor saw me this morning. Why didn't he sign my release?' Sarah demanded in frustration.

'Fear of a cerebral haemorrhage,' came the clipped reply.

Which gave Sarah pause for thought. 'Is there any real risk of that?' she asked uncertainly.

The sister shrugged. 'Slight. But no doctor or hospital wants to risk being sued for not taking proper care.'

Looking after their own interests more than hers. Sarah decided irritably. She didn't even have a headache. It was ridiculous that she had to stay here when she was perfectly well. 'Can't I write some statement releasing everyone from being responsible for my health?' she demanded.

The day sister's face set into sour disapproval. 'There is a form you can sign if that is your wish, but I strongly advise against it.'

But the need for positive action was too strong for Sarah to heed the advice. She wanted to get moving and move she did. However, by the time she had fulfilled the necessary formalities and got dressed it was already past nine o'clock. She would be hideously late for work, but better late than let Frances Chatfield have another day to work her poison, Sarah firmly reasoned.

Fortunately she had enough money in her handbag to pay the taxi fare into the city. Despite the small fortune it would cost her, she didn't feel she could afford to wait for a slow train from Penrith. Nor did she feel there was any point in waiting for Ben to turn up. He hadn't turned up last night. He could easily catch up with her ... if he wanted to.

While she waited for the taxi to arrive Sarah was

called back to the reception desk. Her heart gave a delighted skip when one of the clerks directed her to a telephone, but when she lifted the receiver it was not Ben's voice that greeted her, but Julian's.

'How are you, Sarah?' he asked on a note of concern.

'I'm fine, thank you, Julian,' she answered politely.

'I went to the apartment to see you last night, but no one was at home, and I didn't find out about your accident until this morning. We must talk, Sarah. This can't go on.'

Sarah immediately bridled at his dictatorial tone. 'Julian, I've just checked out of the hospital and I'm waiting for a taxi to take me to work. It'll turn up any minute now. I'm sorry, but talking is not going to make any difference to how I feel. Thank you for calling, but . . .'

'I'll see you tonight,' he said determinedly.

Sarah heaved a sigh of frustration. 'Julian, please don't do that. It's over.'

'I've been talking to Angela. I know all about her brother.'

Sarah could hear the resentment in his voice and tried to set him straight. 'Whatever Angela told you has nothing to do with us. Please, just let it go, Julian.'

'I suppose you had a great laugh at my expense.'

Her heart sank. 'No. I'm sorry you see it that

way. I was only trying to——'

'Taxi for Miss Woodley!'

She waved at the cabbie whose head was poked enquiringly round the reception door. 'I'm sorry, Julian. I have to go now. My taxi's here and I'm late for work as it is.'

'That's right! Put your job ahead of——'

She hung up. She knew it was rude. She angrily hoped it was unforgivable. There simply wasn't any point in going round and round the same futile arguments.

As she hurried out to the taxi Sarah was surprised to find that she was not quite as well as she had thought. Her knees had a disconcerting tendency to turn quite jelly-like, and her head spun a little at any sharp movement. It was probably the effect of having lain in bed too long, she decided, but was glad she had called a taxi. She could relax and rest all the way to the door of the department store.

Despite her good intentions, Sarah could not relax during the trip. She fretted over not having got the Penny Walker contract. Something had to be done. She couldn't just let it go. She alighted from the taxi, imbued with a sense of purpose, but as soon as she entered the store, Sarah knew something was wrong.

She was on friendly terms with most of her fellow workers, but there was an uneasiness in their reaction to her greetings. Was it the unusual lateness of her arrival that made them look shifty, Sarah wondered, or had the scene on Saturday morning plus her absence yesterday generated rumours that suggested a cautious manner might be wise? Store politics could be very tricky at times.

Sarah was not left in doubt for very long—only as long as it took her to reach the Young Trends department. The jolt was so comprehensive she stood rooted to the spot in sheer disbelief. All her displays had been changed! The whole upmarket thrust of the department had been diluted to the point that it had no visual impact at all.

For a few shaky moments Sarah thought she was going to faint. It was the shock of seeing all her work undone, on top of the residual shock of the accident, she reasoned sternly, in a desperate attempt to pull herself together. She couldn't appear weak now. Her sales assistants had noted her arrival and were watching her, waiting warily for her reaction.

Sarah beckoned over Ashley Thompson, who shared Sarah's own enthusiasm for innovative fashions. 'Who organised this abomination, Ashley?'

'Mrs Chatfield.'

It could have been no one else, Sarah knew, but it was as well to have absolute confirmation.

'I'm sorry, Sarah, but there was nothing we

could do about it,' Ashley explained in anxious sympathy.

'Not your responsibility,' Sarah nodded and handed over her handbag and overnight bag. 'Take care of these for me, will you? I'm about to do battle.'

'Sarah, be carful,' Ashley warned. 'She's out to get you.'

Sarah conjured up a reassuring smile. 'Well, I'm not got yet! I'll take this showdown right to the top and no way will I back down this time. Wish me luck, Ashley.'

Her speech won a relieved grin from the girl. 'You can call on our support if you think it'll do any good.'

'Thanks,' Sarah said gratefully, 'but this is strictly executive business and I aim to keep it on that level. It's best for you and the others to keep your noses clean. A job is a job, Ashley.'

'What about you?'

'I do not wish to work under Frances Chatfield's thumb,' Sarah declared decisively and, as she strode off with all the grim purpose of a determined combatant, she added, 'And I will not.'

She felt the same seething fury that she had felt with Julian last Friday. She had not been prepared to live under his thumb, either. If she was forced to break with the store she would, and to hell with the consequences. For years she had been diplomatic and tactful. For years she had struggled to build her department into what it was. She was not going to stand back and allow Frances Chatfield to negate all of that in just one day.

CHAPTER EIGHT

SARAH swept through the Ladies' Fashion department, her gaze flicking from side to side in single-minded search for Frances Chatfield. The sight of Julian conversing amicably with her antagonist came as another body blow. Sarah's stomach knotted. Her head whirled with possible implications, but whatever this double confrontation might mean there was no way she either could or would avoid it now.

Sarah barely hesitated in her step. Pride and determined aggression lifted her chin. She marched towards them without any outward display of concern, but the blood was pounding through her ears like a martial drum calling her to battle.

Somehow they sensed her approach before she reached them. Both heads swung towards her simultaneously. Mutual satisfaction was stamped on their faces. As they turned to face her, Sarah noted the glint of smug triumph in Frances Chatfield's eyes.

Julian took a step forward, holding out his hand to Sarah. 'Mrs Chatfield has just been telling me of the latest reorganisation. The end result will . . .'

'This is not your business, Julian,' Sarah cut in swiftly. 'It's mine!' She focused her attention entirely on the woman at his side. 'Good morning, Frances.' It was the first time she had ever called the older woman by her first name, deliberately denying her superior status.

Frances Chatfield's eyes hardened. A disdainful smile curled her lips. 'You're very late, Sarah. What is your excuse?'

The silky condescension of her tone barely sheathed the smug snipe in the words. Sarah grimly controlled the bristling hostility that surged through her and spoke with measured calmness. 'If I need an excuse, Frances, I'll be giving it to Howard Bowman directly, not to you.'

The smile took on a superior tilt. 'On the contrary, you will report to me, my dear. I promised Howard I'd eradicate this malingering, and he has given me the responsibility of handling all such conflicts with company interests on this floor.'

Not by a flicker of an eyelid did Sarah betray her inner dismay. 'I don't believe you,' she said flatly.

The smile moved into a full-blown sneer. 'Then you're in for a shock, aren't you? After the conference on Friday, and what happened on Saturday morning, it was decided you might be a trifle . . . unreliable.' She rolled out the word with rich relish, pausing over it for maximum effect before continuing. 'Your non-attendance at work yesterday tended to confirm that opinion. Young Trends is being given back to me as part of my responsibilities.'

'And you took it upon yourself to change my displays,' Sarah bit out in barely contained fury.

'Of course. Since I'll be accountable for——'

The fury exploded. 'You're a fool, Frances! It's my department until Howard Bowman tells me otherwise. If what you say is true, then you'd better get him down here straight away, because I'm going back to Young Trends right now to remove that incredibly insipid choice of clothes. And I will not tolerate your interference, so don't try it. Don't ever try to interfere with me again.'

She had swung on her heel and was off before Frances could open her mouth. A hand caught her shoulder. She shrugged it off and whirled with one hand already raised to ward off any further detention, but it was Julian who had hurried after her.

'This is another reckless decision, Sarah. Can't you see what a fool you'll make of yourself? Which is precisely what you've been doing ever since last Friday,' he added with pointed resentment. 'If you'll only listen to me!'

'I listened to you for too long,' she snapped, impatient with his self-serving interference.

'Dammit, Sarah! Can't you see? You've even failed at this job that's so important to you. Don't fight it. Let Frances do it. You're well out of it.'

'I didn't ask for your opinion, Julian, nor do I want it,' she retorted fiercely.

She swung away from him, but again he caught her back. 'I want us to get back together, Sarah. I know all about Ben Haviland. You can't use him as a red herring any more, so ——'

'A red herring!' Sarah scorned. 'You don't know anything, Julian! Now take your hands off me because I have other more important things to attend to.'

She marched off but he trailed in her wake, riled into retaliation. 'Finished, are we? It'll be you and Haviland who'll be finished if you take up with him. I promise you that. I'll break him if it's the last thing I do. He won't get away from me as easily as he did from Frances.'

Sarah paused and rounded on him. 'Don't tangle with Ben, Julian. He's a lot bigger than you. In every way,' she added scathingly, then wished she had held her tongue.

Julian's eyes narrowed. 'You'd take him just for his money, wouldn't you?'

'No!' She was appalled at having led him to think any such thing. It suddenly hit her that not once had she been really tactful or kind to Julian over ending their long relationship. For the most part, she had simply reacted against his arrogant selfishness. She owed him more consideration than that. They had shared a lot of happy times together and it was wrong to end it all with such bitter hostility. With a softer voice and an apologetic expression she tried to mitigate the hurt she had given him.

'I'm sorry, Julian. The decision I made on Friday must have come as a shock to you. I was upset by various things at the time and I didn't behave well, but it wasn't a reckless decision. I've had doubts about how our marriage would work out ever since we became engaged. It was a mistake on my part, and I apologise very sincerely for it. I was trying too hard to be the kind of woman you wanted. But I'm not that kind of woman, Julian, and——'

'I can see that,' he cut in bitterly.

Sarah took a deep breath. 'Then you can see it wouldn't have worked between us,' she finished, determinedly maintaining a soft tone. 'Please excuse me now. There can't be any good purpose served over our aguing any further. I hope you will find someone else who'll suit you better.'

'Like you found Ben Haviland,' Julian sneered at her.

Sarah stared back at him for several seconds, realising that the damage done was irrevocable and there was nothing she could now do or say to appease Julian. She turned away and hurried towards Young Trends, not glancing back, hoping against hope that Julian would just give up and go away. She hadn't handled the break-up well. In fact she was now ashamed of the hostility she had displayed. No matter what the provocation, she should have given Julian more leeway for a dignified exit from her life.

But there was no time for self-castigation now. She had to take positive steps to counteract Frances Chatfield's sly manoeuvring. If the older woman really did have Howard Bowman's support, then Sarah would very shortly be confronting the managing director himself, and she intended to have some ammunition of her own ready.

'I want the clothes we had on this central display as fast as you can find them,' she told Ashley Thompson who was instantly alert to Sarah's return.

'Only be a minute,' Ashley replied eagerly.

Sarah began to undress the models.

'I'm beginning to think you're right about finishing our relationship, Sarah,' Julian's voice said behind her. 'Only a fool would go against Frances, and I don't want to be associated with a fool.'

'Then why don't you go?' she suggested coldly, not pausing in her work even to glance at him.

'Because I want to watch you get your come-uppance.'

Sarah swallowed down the sour bile that almost gorged her throat. It had been Julian himself who had triggered this conflict with his telephone call on Friday, and she was the one paying for his self-indulgence. It took every ounce of control she had not to turn around and stick him with the pins she had gathered in her hand. Ashley Thompson's return with the fashion outfits she wanted was a very timely distraction.

With Ashley's help, Sarah managed to reclothe the models before Frances arrived with Howard Bowman in tow. Sarah took up her stand right next to the display and greeted the managing director with every outward show of confidence, aware that Julian, as well as her assistants, were hovering in the background. She went straight into the attack, refusing him the opportunity to suggest a change of venue for a more private discussion.

'Mr Bowman, I do not appreciate having my department sabotaged by a person who has no understanding whatsoever of what young people want in fashion today.'

'Sabotage is a strong word, Sarah. You should have come to me when you arrived this morning and I would have explained the situation to you,' he replied in an appeasing tone.

'I told Sarah to see you, Howard,' Frances

Chatfield declared primly. 'Her insubordination cannot be tolerated.'

Howard Bowman frowned at Frances, then attempted to project concern at Sarah. 'The fact of the matter is, we have given your position a lot of thought, Sarah. Obviously you are not really a career person. Frances is. And in the long term we think it better if she is responsible——'

'Responsible for what, Mr Bowman?' Sarah cut in scathingly. 'Responsible for watering down this department to an insipid reflection of her own? Just take a good, considered look around you. Every display on this floor, bar this one, is Frances Chatfield's idea of what the young should be buying. But the young, Mr Bowman, have not yet joined the twin-set brigade. Their tastes and wants are different. A whole generation different!' She took a deep breath and added forcefully, 'Which department is making more money?'

His frown deepened as he cast his eye around. 'Well, I ... er ... really think we should talk about this in private.'

Sarah was determined not to budge. 'The figures tell their own story, Mr. Bowman. You know that for the floor area covered I've run the most profitable department in the clothing field. I've got the results on the books, and I think it's about time that the executive board appreciated those figures. In fact, I meant to raise the Penny Walker contract again this morning, because this store is going to lose very badly if we don't tie up a deal with her. You only get such a golden opportunity once.'

Howard Bowman looked even more uncomfortable. He glanced worriedly at Frances Chatfield, who sensed her advantage slipping. 'You know what the decision was on Friday, Howard,' she reminded him waspishly. 'And if you don't back me up now, I'll report everything that has happened to the chairman.'

'The chairman wasn't impressed with you on Friday, Sarah,' Howard agreed ponderously. 'And of course your unexplained absence yesterday . . .'

'She should be fired,' Frances shot in malevolently. 'It's her or me, Howard. You've got ample proof of how unreliable she is. And you can see how insolently she is treating me now.'

The effort already expended on her defence had made Sarah feel dizzy. She clutched at her head in an attempt to keep it steady enough to continue the fight. 'My absence yesterday——'

'Sarah!'

The loud, urgent cry startled them all, and they turned towards it. Ben Haviland was charging across the department floor, and the sight of him brought such a surge of relief to Sarah that her knees wobbled. He had said he would come to her today and he had kept his word.

'Ben?' she breathed hopefully, her hand instinctively reaching out to him.

He swept her up in this arms, cradling her with tender care as he anxiously scaned her face. 'Don't ever do that to me again!' he commanded. 'You've had me worried crazy. When Penny and I got to the hospital and you weren't there . . .'

'Penny?' Sarah asked a little dazedly. It was wonderful to have Ben's arms around her again, and he cared about her. He really did care. But what was he doing with her favourite dress-designer?

'I brought her along to talk business with you. But you'd left. You shouldn't be here, Sarah. The doctors warned me you could have a cerebral haemorrhage. What are you thinking of, taking such a risk with our future?'

Our future. What beautiful words they were, Sarah thought happily.

'You're coming home with me right now,' continued Ben. 'And no argument. I'm going to make sure you take proper care of yourself, even if I have to stand over you every minute of the day and night.'

'What on earth is going on?' Howard Bowman blustered. 'What hospital? And what's all this about a cerebral haemorrhage?'

Ben glowered at him. 'Who are you?'

'I'm the managing director of this store.'

'Then you ought to be horse-whipped for letting Sarah come back to work.'

Howard instantly took umbrage. 'Kindly explain that statement. I'll have you know——'

'What do you run here? A slave-factory?' Ben cut in contemptuously. 'The car accident on Sunday wasn't Sarah's fault, and if you ...'

'I wasn't told anything about a car accident!'

Ben glared accusingly at Frances Chatfield. 'Angela telephoned you. You knew Sarah was suffering from concussion. I suppose you wanted her dead too, just like poor old Tramp.'

'How dare you!' Frances spluttered.

'I think you'd better explain yourself, Frances,' Howard Bowman said curtly. 'You gave me to understand that Sarah ...'

'Don't believe a word Frances tells you. She's a liar!' Ben spat in disgust.

'And you're a fraud, Haviland!' Julian stepped from the sidelines and placed himself at Frances Chatfield's side, his expression one of triumphant malevolence. 'I know all about your tax avoidance scheme and I'm going to take you to the cleaners,' he gloated.

'No!' Sarah cried, so alarmed on Ben's behalf that she struggled against the warm security of his embrace. 'You have to let me go, Ben. I know how much you hate pressures. I can't marry you if it's going to ruin you.'

He smiled and clutched her more tightly. 'Don't you worry about a thing, Sarah. He can't touch us.'

'Oh, yes, I can,' Julian sniped. 'I've got the evidence of your sister that any marriage you enter into is completely bogus, just to split your income.'

'Angela!' Ben said in surprise, then laughed out loud. 'Good God, man! Angela's the greatest practical joker in the world. If she said that, she was pulling your leg. And you fell for it!'

'She was serious!' Julian insisted fiercely. 'And that's avoidence, Haviland. A bogus marriage won't wash with the tax department. I'll get you on Section 260A.'

'And I'll back him up.' Frances hurled in. 'I'll bear witness to what an artful dodger you are, Ben Haviland. You promised to marry me once, and——'

'You're right, Frances,' Ben agreed, his face suddenly puckering in concern. 'That was a terrible thing I did to you and I'm sorry. It was very wrong, running away like that. Cowardly. I've only just started to grow up and appreciate how badly I treated you, and I'm deeply ashamed that I didn't handle the differences between us in a more kindly and considerate way. I don't expect you to forgive me . . .'

'No, I won't!' she shot at him, not the least bit mollified by his apology.

'And neither will I for what you've done to Sarah,' Julian sniped.

'I'm sorry. I'm sorry for both of you,' Ben said in

another attempt at appeasement. 'But I can't change what's happened. Sarah and I love each other, and ...'

Julian gave a mocking laugh. 'That's impossible! You've barely met.'

'It's true, none-the-less,' Ben stated seriously. 'Now, if you'll excuse us, I'm taking Sarah home. She's not well and shouldn't be here.'

'Now just a minute——' Howard Bowman began.

But Ben didn't let him finish. 'You've had your chance. You should have seen Sarah's worth and promoted her. I'm going to put her in her own boutique. Let her run it as she sees fit.' He turned back to Julian with a last word of well-meant advice. 'And as for trying to prove a bogus marriage, you'll find yourself a laughing stock when Sarah's expecting our first baby.'

Julian glared at Sarah. 'You gold-digging bitch! You've slept with him already!'

'If I wasn't holding Sarah, you'd pay for that,' Ben growled at him. 'You'd better keep out of Sarah's way in future, or so help me God, I'll drop you from the tallest building I can find. Without benefit of clergy or parachute!'

And with that he started to stride off, carrying Sarah like a precious prize that he'd never let go. Sarah's mind registered a slightly out-of-focus picture: Julian, an alien figure of furious frustration, Frances, the scrupulously put-together fashion-plate with her polished veneer cracking at the seams, Howard Bowman, affronted dignity stamped all over his posture, and behind them the display that Sarah had changed to reflect all that she herself had stood for. And Ben was carrying her away, away from the past and into their future, she thought with a mild sense of hysteria.

'Ben, I've got to get my bags,' she protested, even as she wound her arms around his neck in heartfelt gratitude for his wonderful support.

'Angela can get them later. We're going home, where you'll be safe from people like that.'

She snuggled her head on to his broad shoulder and wondered why she was accepting it all so passively. She had broken up with Julian over her job, fought with Frances to keep it, confronted the managing director himself, but she didn't mind at all that Ben had swept the whole thing aside. Either she really had gone weak in the head or ... No, it was because he had proved he really cared about her. He had stood up to all three of her antagonists and fought them for her sake. Master of the situation, she thought with blissful pride, even against Frances.

They had to wait for an elevator and Ben's mouth brushed warmly over her hair. 'Sarah, are you feeling bad?' he asked anxiously.

'Not now you're here,' she murmured contentedly.

The doors opened and he carried her into the small compartment where they were entirely alone. Ben held her a little more tightly and Sarah didn't feel the least bit suffocated by his closeness. She felt wonderfully cherished.

'Why did you come back here?' Ben asked, his voice vibrating with concern. 'I thought you were safe at the hospital.'

'I was worried about my job, and I thought . . . I thought *you* might have had second thoughts, Ben.'

'I told you I'd come to the hospital today,' he reminded her chidingly.

Sarah heaved a regretful sigh that she hadn't waited for him. 'Well, you didn't come last night, and Angela said that maybe I shouldn't rely on you. I'm sorry, Ben, but things have been happening so fast, I just wasn't sure.'

'Angela's getting to be a damned busybody,' he muttered grimly.

The elevator doors opened on the ground floor and Ben strode out again, making for the Pitt Street exit. 'Penny's got a taxi waiting for us. I took her to the hospital with me to discuss the boutique with you, but when you were missing . . .' He dragged in a sharp breath. 'I know I said you could come and go as you please, Sarah, but next time, would you tell me first? It did terrible things to my stomach, not knowing where you were.'

'Same thing for me, Ben,' she said in soft appeal. 'It did terrible things to my stomach last night, not knowing what you were doing. Or thinking.'

He frowned, obviously giving the matter deep thought as he continued out to the pavement where the taxi was waiting for them.

Penny Walker jumped out of the back seat, her fresh young face a picture of relief. 'You found her!' she cried.

'Penny, I think we'd better leave our business until tomorrow,' Ben said quickly. 'Would you mind?'

'Of course not. Give me a call when Sarah feels up to it. You take the taxi and I'll find my own way home.'

'Thanks, Penny,' he accepted gratefully, and bundled Sarah into the taxi without pause, giving the driver their home address even as he waved goodbye to Penny.

Sarah laid her head back against the seat, feeling rather drained by all the morning's emotional activity. Ben wrapped his hand around hers in a warmly possessive way. He did not relax, and for a few moments his uneasiness unsettled her, until he spoke.

'Sarah, I'm sorry about worrying you yesterday. I didn't tell you what I was planning because I wasn't sure how much I could do, but once I met

Penny things got rolling pretty fast and I was so anxious to get you out of that store. I know how much you like being in the fashion busines, but I couldn't stand the thought of you going back to work with that poisonous woman.'

The warm surge of happiness pulsed from Sarah's heart. 'You were thinking of me?'

Ben's mouth curved in bemusement. 'I can't think of anything else. I thought if I could get your boutique set up before you got out of hospital, you'd be happy to give up your job at the store.' His eyes appealed for forgiveness. 'I guess I shouldn't have said you were resigning, but when I looked at Frances, I couldn't bear you to be even near her any more. But I shouldn't have pushed what I wanted on to you. If you want to go back . . .?'

'No.' She smiled her pleasure in him. 'I thought you were marvellous, the way you stood up to Frances and told her off.'

He sighed in relief. 'I'd do anything for you, Sarah. And I wanted to come to you last night, but I had this sense of urgency over setting you up in the business you wanted, and Penny organised a meeting with these other young designers she reckons are good. I figured if Penny thought so you would, too. And they'd all be happy to stock your boutique, Sarah. All you've got to do is give them a deadline. And I've got a list of shops for lease that you can choose from . . .'

He stopped as Sarah started to laugh. 'Oh, Ben!' she gasped. 'You've got me on that roller-coaster again!'

He looked perplexed. 'What roller-coaster?'

'The one you've had me riding on ever since we met.'

He frowned. 'Am I going too fast for you, Sarah?'

'I do feel a little dizzy,' she confessed.

'I'm talking too much. You just rest. I've got to take care of you,' he said in quick concern, then settled back, determinedly silent, although his hand fondled hers with a persistent sense of possessiveness.

Sarah marvelled at all he had done for her. What other man who had no first-hand experience of the fashion world would have plunged into it as Ben had, just to protect her and please her? What other man had ever really listened to her ideas and taken appreciative note of them? Or made her feel so cared for? And the most wonderful part was, she knew with absolute certainty, that it wasn't all a false front to coax her into marriage. Ben was no actor. What you saw was what you got. And he really was marvellous.

When the taxi pulled up at their apartment block at Neutral Bay, Ben was out like a flash and round at her door before Sarah had even moved. He handed the driver the fare, then scooped Sarah up into his arms again.

'I can walk, Ben,' she demurred weakly.

'Not if you're dizzy. I'm going to put you straight to bed, Sarah. No more risks today,' he insisted.

She wasn't really dizzy. Not physically dizzy. It was only her emotions that were spinning like crazy, but Sarah didn't correct Ben. She hung on to him, secretly revelling in his strength and tenderness, and when he ultimately carried her into her bedroom and gently laid her on the bed, she did not want to unlock her arms from around his neck. His mouth was close to her own, and the sensual curve of his lips reminded her very forcefully of what even their lightest touch could do to her.

'Thank you for everything, Ben,' she whispered.

'Sarah . . .' Her name was a strained breath of need, mingling with hers.

The temptation was too great to resist. Even as she pulled his head down to hers, it flashed through her mind that she was inviting trouble. But it seemed so long since he had last kissed her, and right now, she needed that more than anything else in the world. The urgent, searching pressure of his lips against her own took Sarah's breath away. Little shivers of excitement ran down her spine. She could not stop her hands from sliding over his strongly muscled back, pressing him closer to her, wanting the deepening of his kiss, wanting . . .

Ben suddenly broke away, the separation so abrupt that Sarah was stunned by a sharp sense of bereftness. She stared up at him, eyes glazed with unsatisfied passion. His chest was heaving as he dragged in gasping breaths. He groaned and gathered her up to him in a crushing embrace, his cheek rubbing against hers in an agony of longing.

'I need you, Sarah. I want you so much I'm going insane thinking about you all the time. I can't control it and I don't even want to control it. I don't even care about the money anymore. Only you. Only you.'

His fingers threaded through her hair and gently tugged her head back. His eyes glittered feverishly, desire fighting with an intensity of purpose that begged her understanding. 'I'm not going to rush you, Sarah. I'll wait for ever for you. I want you to be sure. I couldn't bear it if you weren't happy with me.'

'But——'

'No, listen to me!' he pleaded, with so much pent-up feeling that Sarah held her tongue. 'I'll pay whatever is necessary, and I'll wait for you as long as it takes because I don't want to live without you. We'll do whatever you want, I promise you. And I'll try to be everything you want.'

'Oh, Ben! You are. You are everything I want,' Sarah cried, knowing in that moment that she had never spoken a greater truth. And she kissed him with all the exultant conviction in her heart and soul.

She felt the shudder of passion run through Ben's body as he bore her back down to the pillow and followed her, his heavy, powerful legs covering hers, his broad, muscular chest almost flattening the soft fullness of her breasts. But she didn't care. She hugged him even closer, glorying in the hard, male strength of him, responding fiercely to the wild hunger of his mouth and the feverish caress of his hands.

His legs entwined with hers, holding her to him as he shifted on to his side. His hand closed over her breast, softly kneading it into swelling sensitivity. He rained kisses over her face, gasping incoherent words of need and want, and Sarah surrendered to it all with a savage joy that rampaged through her veins and melted all her bones.

She cried an instinctive protest when Ben made to pull away from her. He groaned as he resisted the frantic clutch of her hands. 'Sarah . . . Sarah . . .' Harsh agonised bursts of breath. 'I shouldn't be doing this. The excitement . . . it might kill you.'

A great welling of love pumped from her heart. 'It's strong medicine, Ben,' she whispered, then more urgently, 'I need you. I need you.'

'Oh, God!' he moaned, and restraint was flung to the winds.

Sarah felt no embarrassment, no twinge of

shame as Ben undressed her, and when he undressed himself, the revelation of his magnificent body sent quivers of excitement through her. For the first time in her life she felt a glorious sense of rightness in this intimate sharing of nakedness: man and woman ... as they were made for each other ... to touch, to hold, to join, to be as one.

She welcomed him with all that she was, answering the urgency of his need with an explosion of passion that exulted in every touch, every movement, every pressure. And nothing, nothing in the whole of creation, could have been more right than their possession of each other, their bodies driving together in an ecstatic fusion that shattered every barrier of self and tipped them into another incredible dimension of feeling where neither could exist without the other.

They lay together for a long time, blissfully content, lightly touching in soft wonderment as they thought their own thoughts. If she had really had any doubts about falling in love with Ben Haviland, they had all been put behind her now. Sarah knew he was her man for the rest of her life. Never had she known such completeness, such utter fulfilment as a woman. How could there be anyone else like him?

She nestled closer, rubbing her cheek across his shoulder, kissing the pulse at the base of his throat. His arm came around her, holding her there, wanting her there. She smiled her contentment.

'Ben?' she murmured, reluctant to break the beautiful harmony of their silence.

'Mmm?' It was a hum of blissful satisfaction.

Her smile gathered a happy indulgence. 'I think we should get married straight away and save the money.'

Ben's arm hugged her even closer. 'Nothing I'd like better, but, Sarah, don't get me wrong now . . . that thirtieth of June date doesn't apply any more. It never really did. So if you want more time . . .'

She lifted her head in surprise. 'Never really applied? You said it was terribly important and urgent.'

'Only you are important, my love.' His fingers played a delicately sensuous tune on her spine, and his smile widened into a joyful grin. 'And urgent. But the fact is that Julian will get his pound of flesh, no matter what. Besides, as I said before, I don't give a damn about the money as long as I have you. I want you to name whatever date you like.'

Sarah stared at him. 'But if we can save all that money by marrying straight away, then . . .'

'Sarah, please, forget the damned money!' He sounded almost goaded, then added defiantly, 'The tax thing never had anything to do with why I asked you to marry me.'

'Never?' The word came out as an outraged squawk as Sarah recalled all the worrying she had done over his financial problems.

Ben's face screwed into a rueful appeal. 'I couldn't think of anything else fast enough and I had to get your mind off Julian. Give you something else to think about, so you wouldn't get depressed and want him back. I figured if I could get you to see me as husband material straight away, I'd have more chance with you. And since you were obviously a businesswoman, I thought the money angle might intrigue you.'

His eyes begged her understanding. 'It was a hell of a spot to be in, Sarah, meeting the woman you've been looking for all your life and finding her hung up on some other guy. I was desperate. I've never worked so hard, trying to give you all the right options and answers to get you concentrating on me. It was like threading through a minefield. But I never once lied to you about the kind of relationship we'll have, Sarah,' he added anxiously. 'I'd do anything in the world to ensure you stay happy with me.'

'Oh, Ben!' The sigh turned into a rueful smile. He was so irresistibly wonderful that she instantly forgave him all his schemes. 'I think you must be the most marvellous inventor in the whole world, and I don't care about anything else either. I still want us to get married straight away,' she insisted firmly, and saw in his eyes his blissful joy in her, the love that made everything else unimportant.

'Best thing,' he agreed happily. 'Do it as soon as we can!'

And in the kiss that sealed their agreement was the promise of the most positive future there could ever be for a man and a woman who had found their true mate in each other.

CHAPTER NINE

'HOLD on a minute! I can't believe this!' Angela threw up her hands, pushed herself out of the armchair, and started pacing the living-room floor, a worried frown creasing her brow.

'It's true,' Ben said, looking down at Sarah for support.

She was snuggled next to him on the sofa and she nodded her head in agreement. 'It just happened. There was nothing either of us could do about it. It's got nothing to do with Ben's original situation, Angela,' she assured her friend.

'Not even going to have a marriage contract,' Ben added for good measure. 'In fact, I shouldn't have even mentioned it. Don't know why I even thought of it. It got Sarah all confused and unhappy about marrying me. But we've got it all straightened out now. Everything's perfect, isn't it, Sarah?'

She smiled her love up at him and Ben beamed his right back at her.

Angela confronted her brother with mounting exasperation. 'Do you realise I've been working my butt off, cajoling, flattering, imploring and pleading in order to get someone to marry you? And now you're going to marry my best friend!'

'I did warn you,' Ben pointed out. 'It's your fault if you don't listen. I told you to cancel——'

'But at that time Sarah said she wasn't marrying you,' Angela argued.

'I never believed it!' Ben declared. 'You didn't mean it, did you, Sarah?'

'Well, I was a bit confused . . .'

'And rightly so. My fault,' Ben stated grandly, completely exonerating her from any blame whatsoever.

Sarah breathed a happy sigh. It was marvellous having Ben think she was perfect. Of course, there might come a time when he changed his mind about that, but Sarah firmly resolved to make him keep thinking it as long as it was humanly possible.

Angela stared down at them, still shaking her head. 'Well, I suppose I can cope with being made to look foolish. What I find most alarming is you two.'

Ben looked surprised. 'Nothing wrong with us, is there, Sarah?'

But Angela wasn't mollified. 'Now don't start that again!' she whipped out. 'For all your waywardness, Ben, you are my brother, and I love you for that reason if for no other. And Sarah is my best friend. I hate the thought of both of you making each other miserable for the rest of your lives because of some mistaken notion . . .'

'It's not a mistaken notion,' Ben cut in, affronted at the very idea. 'It was love at first sight. Didn't believe in it until it happened. But when I saw Sarah I said to myself, that's the woman I want and if I can't have her, I don't want any other.'

'And Ben certainly had a strong effect on me from the very first meeting,' Sarah insisted.

'You've got no idea what it's like, Angela.' Ben hit a fist into the palm of his other hand in illustration. 'Like being smacked over the head with a sledge-hammer.'

'Or being thrown out of the window on the fourth floor,' Sarah laughed, remembering her feeling of being on a runaway roller-coaster.

Angela still looked slightly sceptical. 'Are you two certain it's love and not just strong attraction?'

'Both!' said Ben, very positively. 'Of course we'll have our differences. We've had them already. But we're very good at sorting them out, aren't we, Sarah? And that's because we love each other, Angela. There's nothing I want more than Sarah to be happy with me, and no one can say or do anything that will ever change that.'

Angela looked a little dazed by this speech. She heaved a sigh and dropped back into her armchir. She lifted her hand in a helpless gesture as if to say it was all beyond her but she had done her best and what more could she do? 'Well, I suppose you want me to vacate the apartment,' she said vaguely.

'Of course not. I bought it for you, didn't I? I've never been an Indian giver, Angela,' Ben chided her.

Angela offered an apologetic grimace. 'Sorry. You've just knocked me for five. Or six. Or seven. I don't know what to think any more.'

'Sarah and I are going to buy a big house on a double block,' Ben announced. 'And then we're going to fill it with kids.'

'And two dogs,' Sarah added to complete the picture.

Ben grinned happily at her. 'Maybe more. Depends on what the kids want.'

Angela looked incredulously at Ben. 'Is this really my maverick brother?'

He shot her a serious look. 'Well, it's like this, Angela. Sarah showed me a whole new way of looking at things. I was missing out, you know. Didn't even see it until I met Sarah. I owe her an awful lot.'

Sarah squeezed his hand in blissful contentment. 'You showed me some good things too, Ben.'

His hand squeezed back. 'We were meant for each other, Sarah.'

'So, when's the wedding?' Angela asked, resigning herself to the inevitable.

'Twenty-fifth of June,' Ben answered promptly. 'And we've got to start getting organised.'

The doorbell rang and Angela looked suspiciously at Ben and Sarah as she rose to her feet. 'Is this another one of your surprises?' she demanded rhetorically, and opened the door with a theatrical flourish. 'I hope you don't want to marry Ben,' she tossed flippantly at the doorbell-ringer. 'Because he's already spoken for.'

'No, not at all,' came the startled reply. 'I work at the store with Sarah and she left her bags behind, so I thought . . .'

'Ashley!' Sarah jumped up to welcome her. 'Come on in.' She quickly introduced her to Angela and Ben and thanked her for her kindness in bringing the bags from the store. 'Have you time to stop a while? I guess I owe you and the other girls an apology for deserting the ship, so to speak.'

Ashley laughed as she dropped into an armchair. 'Actually we all felt like clapping. You sure socked it to them, Sarah. You and Ben,' she added, her eyes sparkling with admiration.

For the next half-hour Ashley regaled them with all the reactions of everyone at the store after Ben and Sarah had made their dramatic exit. Angela, having heard nothing of this morning's scene, kept prompting Ashley for every detail, and ended up rolling around the floor in helpless paroxysms of laughter.

'It wasn't all that funny,' Sarah chided her. 'In

fact, the situation before Ben arrived was really rather nasty.'

Ashley nodded agreement. 'It certainly was, and to tell you the truth, Sarah, I want to resign too, now that Mrs Chatfield's taking over. I was wondering if you'd consider me if you want a sales assistant when you open your boutique.'

Sarah looked at Ben and they both nodded together.

'Won't be until the end of July, Ashley,' Ben warned. 'Sarah reckons we should open the boutique with Penny Walker's spring collection and we need the time before then to get married, have a honeymoon and set up house.'

'But as soon as we're operational, we'll have you on the payroll,' Sarah assured her happily.

'That's fantastic!' Ashley was so excited she jumped up and kissed them both. 'And congratulations, too! I hope you'll both be very, very happy.'

And on Sarah's promise to keep in touch, Ashley took her leave. As soon as the door was closed behind her, Angela started raising more questions. 'What kind of wedding are you going to have? Register office?'

'No way!' said Ben decisively. 'We're having the full, proper ceremony. We've already broken the news to Sarah's parents and we're going up to Mount Victoria next weekend to get them organised.'

Angela's eyes widened at Sarah. 'How did your mum and dad take all this?'

'They thought it was a bit hasty at first, but we talked them around, didn't we, Ben?' She smiled up at him, and he chuckled in remembrance.

Angela took to shaking her head again. 'Well, if you're really having a proper wedding, you'll have to get Mum and Dad back from overseas. They certainly wouldn't want to miss this. They've been waiting for one or the other of us to marry for years.' She broke into a laugh. 'They sure didn't expect it to be you, Ben!'

'Will you be my bridesmaid, Angela?' Sarah asked eagerly.

'Love to.' Her eyes sparked with a wickedly teasing glint. 'I want all the inside information I can get. If you two end up murdering each other, it'll give me a crime scoop that'll knock my editor's eyes out.'

Ben laughed and hugged Sarah closer. 'Don't get your hopes up, Angela. That's never going to happen. But you can get one of your society reporters to cover the wedding. We've asked Penny Walker to design the dresses for the bridal party and it'll be a good bit of publicity for the boutique.'

Angela gave a bemused laugh. 'When you move, brother, you certainly do move!'

And that thought was to echo through Sarah's mind continually over the next few weeks. They moved at a hectic pace, having meetings with other young designers besides Penny Walker, choosing what Sarah wanted to sell and selecting just the right premises for the boutique. Ben scouted out houses for Sarah to look at and they eventually settled on a beautiful old home at Lane Cove because it had lovely big rooms and a huge garden. Then there was furniture to buy, fittings for her wedding dress, endless details to settle. Ben decided he would not replace the Ferrari with another sports car and turned up with two BMWs, saying they would be more practical for transporting babies and dogs.

After one particularly exhausting day, Sarah could not help remarking, 'For a man who can't stand the thought of having a job, you certainly work hard, Ben.'

He looked surprised. 'But this isn't work! We're creating something. That's a lot different to doing repetitive tasks. I love getting into something new and exciting.' He suddenly eyed her with anxious concern. 'I hope you don't mind my not having a regular job, Sarah, but I'd die if I wasn't doing something creative. Can you really put up with me?'

'I love you just as you are, Ben Haviland. I don't ever want you to change and don't you ever doubt that,' she assured him without the slightest hesitation.

He smiled in relief. 'You know one of the things I love about you, Sarah? You're such a positive person. And I've been thinking about a name for the boutique, something that expresses the whole concept you're after. How about The Positive Approach?'

'That's great!' Sarah threw her arms around his neck in enthusiastic fervour. 'You're a genius, Ben! An absolute genius!'

He laughed. 'If I am, it's you who inspires me.' And he kissed her in such an inspirational way that any kind of work was forgotten for quite some time.

Ben's parents flew home from Europe, absolutely thrilled about their son's marriage plans and delighted to meet Sarah and her family. In fact, Sarah got the distinct impression that they viewed her as some kind of miracle worker, which was a little unsettling. Occasionally she worried if Ben really would be happy with the family life they had planned, but then she would look at him and the doubts and fears melted away. Whatever happened in their future, she couldn't want any man other than Ben.

The wedding was a wonderfully happy occasion. Penny Walker had designed Sarah a magnificent dress in white silk taffeta with an appliquéd motif of pink and silver roses. Angela's deep pink bridesmaid's dress was the perfect complement. Ben was resplendent in silver-grey tails and one of

Sarah's brothers stood in as best man. Angela had not only organised a photographer from her newspaper, but also a friend to video the whole event 'so she could really believe it had actually happened'.

Jack Woodley declared that Ben was just the kind of son-in-law he had hoped to welcome into the family. Ben's father declared that Sarah was a girl in a million, several million in fact, and both mothers wept happy, sentimental tears when Ben and Sarah finally took their leave.

Ben had chosen the Bahamas for their honeymoon, and they spent a blissful three weeks cruising around the Caribbean. Everything was perfect—the weather, the balmy atmosphere of the islands, the tropical splendour around them, and, most of all, the marvellous intimacy of every touch, the instant understanding of every word, every expression of love that they shared.

'We'll have to go home some time,' Sarah said one morning.

'Mmm ... this year or next?' Ben murmured, stroking featherlight fingertips down her spine.

Sarah squirmed with pleasure. 'I'm getting fat and lazy, just lying around doing nothing.'

'You're beautiful, and you're not doing nothing,' Ben breathed huskily as he rolled her over into his arms.

And Sarah forgot to raise the matter again for

over a week. However, a letter from Ashley Thompson and Penny Walker reminded her of her responsibilities, and she felt quite burdened over disturbing Ben about the scheduled opening of the boutique. She was quite sure he had no real interest in ladies' fashions and he had only involved himself because it interested her. At this particular stage, Sarah wondered why she had been so interested herself, but took herself to task for the thought. It would be positively delinquent of her not to fulfil the obligations she had taken on.

Nevertheless, it was with some diffidence that she approached the subject of going home once again. To her surprise Ben agreed instantly, with only one proviso. 'We must stop off in New York on the way.'

'What do you want to do in New York?' Sarah asked, uncaring about what they did as long as it was together. 'Have you got business there?'

'I've been thinking ... We should put in some spadework, Sarah. Got to plan for the future. I know you'll get a lot of pleasure from running your boutique because it's what you've dreamed of, and it's always great for dreams to come true. I know you've got the talent to do it well, but you're like me, Sarah. You'll get bored doing repetitive stuff. What you're really good at is spotting new possibilities in fashion and we should prepare the ground for you becoming an agent and expanding overseas. New York's the place to start.'

'But how? What do I do?' Sarah spluttered, totally stunned by such an idea.

Ben grinned at her. 'The world is just one big market-place. You can take New York, London, even Paris by storm if you've got a mind to. You don't have to, but let's start making an opportunity in case you do want it. We'll drop in on some old friends in New York and set up some contacts. You could become the outstanding agent for new Australian designers and show their designs to the world. Pick the best. Quite exciting really, finding real originals.'

'Oh, Ben! What a fantastic idea!' Sarah breathed, her eyes shining with delight.

He laughed and swung her up in his arms. 'Thought you'd like it.'

'You've done so much for me, Ben. I wish there was something I could do for you.'

He kissed her. 'You're doing everything for me, all the time, just by being you and being with me,' he said with absolute conviction, and Sarah hoped with all her heart that that would be enough for him in all the years ahead.

CHAPTER TEN

THE London collection had been a staggering success, but the euphoria over its acclaim by the fashion world had slowly waned. Sarah was exhausted, and she could hardly wait for the plane to touch down at Mascot Airport where Ben and the children would be waiting for her. She had missed them so much and she was beginning to think that Ben was right about success. There came a time when it could be achieved almost too easily, became almost taken for granted. Maybe she should give the game up now. But there was still Paris . . .

'You're so lucky to have Ben to come home to.'

Sarah glanced her surprise at the young woman sitting beside her. She had thought that Penny would still be riding high. Her designs had won every possible accolade from the most discerning critics in the fashion world. Yet the words had been spoken on a despondent sigh.

'Yes, I am lucky,' Sarah agreed softly. She didn't have Penny Walker's creative brilliance, but not even a talent like that could ever measure up to what Ben gave her. Her heart lifted at the thought of being with him. Soon now.

Penny sighed again. 'The feeling of conquering one of the great bastions, there's nothing like it, yet afterwards . . .' She rolled her head towards Sarah, her mouth curled into an ironic smile. 'I guess I'll put my head down and design more dresses, more collections. That's all I have in my life. But to come home to someone like Ben . . . You've got everything a woman could ever want, Sarah.'

The ache of inner loneliness whispered behind every word and Sarah didn't know how to appease it. She reached over and squeezed Penny's hand. 'You'll find someone who loves you one day. Perhaps in Paris, some fine, dashing Frenchman who'll adore everything about you. He'll burst into your life and suddenly you'll feel you hadn't really lived before you met him.' She smiled in remembrance of her first meeting with Ben. 'I was twenty-eight when Ben swept me off my feet. Literally. You're only twenty-seven now, Penny. You'll meet someone. Some day.'

Penny's smile changed to one of hopeful whimsy. 'Well, I'll look forward to Paris.'

Sarah sank back into her own thoughts. She could no longer imagine a life without Ben. It would soon be their fifth wedding anniversary. She wondered how they would celebrate it this year. Ben always came up with some marvellous idea.

She would do the organisation for Penny's Paris

collection, Sarah decided, but it would definitely be the last. Her swan-song. In a funny kind of way she felt she owed it to Penny. Her mind slipped back to the conference at the store where it had all begun: Julian's call that had messed up Sarah's bid to tie up a contract with Penny. If she hadn't been so incensed by it, hadn't been so keen to get Penny's designs on sale ... No. Ben and she would still have got together. Somehow. As Ben said, they had been made for each other. Still, the issue over Penny's contract had accelerated everything.

Amusement bubbled through her mind as she thought of Julian, married to Frances Chatfield. Ben had chuckled all day when they had heard about it. 'They're well matched so they'll probably be happy,' he had declared.

Sarah actually hoped they were, although she could not imagine any couple being happier than she and Ben. Sometimes it worried her a little that Ben didn't work at a regular job, but he was such an ideal father and he seemed so content doing whatever he was doing ... and he had come up with the whirly-truck that flew, which was still selling well in the toy shops. But that was two years ago when Christopher had been eighteen months old and enchanted with all things mechanical.

Since then ... not that it mattered. Even if Ben never came up with another selling idea, they had enough investments and income from the boutiques to keep them secure for the rest of their lives. Sarah smiled as she thought of Ashley Thompson and how she had taken to boutique management like a duck to water. Ashley was just like one of the family, sharing the apartment with Angela and becoming as involved as Sarah in the fashion business.

And Ben had set it all up. Sarah was quite sure that Ben would find a way to do anything. There was really nothing for her to worry about. And as long as he was happy at home with her and their family ... that was the only important thing.

The jet engines went into reverse and the plane touched down. Sarah heaved a sigh of relief. Home at last. Excitement coursed through her as she joined the stream of passengers making their exit from the plane, and as soon as she set foot inside the terminal she was greeted by a triumphant shout from Christopher.

'Mummy! Mummy!'

The short, three-year-old legs pelted towards her and she swooped on him, catching him up in her arms and hugging him tight, as her gaze automatically searched for Ben. He was standing back, out of the way of the emerging crowd, a huge grin of welcome on his face and Sally perched on his shoulders, waving a chubby little hand at her.

A great surge of love wound around Sarah's heart. Her husband. Her family. 'I saw you first,

Mummy,' Christopher crowed in her ear as she carried him back to Ben. 'Kiss, Mummy,' Sally demanded, and was instantly hoisted from Ben's shoulders and held out to Sarah. Christopher slid down to give place to his little sister and Sarah cuddled her darling daughter and gave her lots of kisses.

'I think it's my turn,' Ben said, his eyes caressing Sarah with a desire that had not diminished at all over the years. She gave Sally into Christopher's charge and sank into Ben's strong embrace, savouring the wonderful sense of belonging he always gave her. 'Welcome home, darling,' he murmured, and his kiss was a sweet reminder of what they would share when the time was right.

They heard Penny talking to their children and quickly turned to gather her into their circle. Ben gave her a mock-salute, 'Hail to the conqueror!' and Penny laughed. 'Knew you were a winner, Penny,' Ben declared. 'Sarah's never wrong. That was a great triumph in London. We're all terribly proud of you.'

And Penny glowed under his congratulations as they all went to collect the luggage. Sarah slipped her arm around Ben's, hugging it possessively, loving him fiercely for being so nice, so kind, so giving. They saw Penny off in a taxi and then finally they were alone together in their own family car.

'We've got a big surprise for you at home, Mummy,' Christopher said excitedly.

'Big s'prise,' echoed Sally with happy emphasis.

Sarah raised her eyebrows at Ben.

'Big surprise,' he said smugly.

It was plain that she was not to be told. Even Christopher and Sally stood firm against her questions, and Ben's grin grew wider and wider. 'We'll show you as soon as we get home,' he promised, and with that she had to be content.

Honey and Tramp barked a feverish welcome from the backyard as they turned into the driveway. However, Sarah was not allowed to go and greet the dogs. The children were in such a fever of excitement by the time they had all alighted from the car that they literally dragged Sarah into the house.

'The family-room, Mummy,' Christopher directed.

'They're all there,' Sally crowed.

Ben threw the door of the family-room open with a flourish and there, sitting on the chairs and cupboards and shelves, was the most extraordinary collection of soft-toy creatures: fantasy animals that had to be the product of brilliant imagination, madly exaggerated, made in brilliant colour combinations, and the expressions on their faces so amusing and endearing that Sarah immediately fell in love with all of them.

'The Trendsetters,' Ben proudly announced.

'We helped Daddy make them up,' Christopher said just as proudly.

'And get the colours,' Sally said importantly.

Sarah gestured her amazement at their cleverness. 'They're the most marvellous creations I've ever seen.'

'We got the girls in Penny's factory to make them up for us while you were away,' Ben informed her with a delighted smile at her reaction. 'They loved them so much they've already put in orders. I think we're on to another big winner, Sarah.'

'Oh, yes!' Sarah agreed very positively. 'No doubt about it!'

Ben sighed. 'Unfortunately, it'll bring us another tax problem, Sarah. So I guess we'd better consider some more income splitting.'

Sarah's delight turned to a threatening glower. 'Now just a minute, Ben Haviland!'

His eyebrows shot up at her tone. 'Well, it's only sensible . . .'

'If you're thinking of becoming a Mormon or a Muslim . . .'

'Whatever for?'

'I've seen your solution to tax problems before, and I won't have you setting up a harem, or marrying another woman just to divide . . .'

He burst out laughing and pulled her into a very

possessive hug. 'As if I would when I've got you, you crazy woman! I was thinking of a trust fund with the children as beneficiaries.'

'Oh!'

'But it's nice to know you don't want to share me,' Ben teased.

The jealous fierceness in her eyes melted into deep wells of love. 'Only with the children.'

And love shone back at her. 'Which reminds me,' Ben murmured huskily. 'I think it's time we got started on our third. If you want to?' It was a gentle question.

'I want to,' she sighed happily.

And much, much later, when Christopher and Sally were safely tucked into bed for the night, Ben rolled her into his arms and held her close. 'It's so good to have you home. Do you know why I love you so much?' he murmured.

Sarah reached up to touch his face, her fingers lightly tracing the tiny scar in his eyebrow, the dimples in his cheeks, the full sensual lips, caressing, loving. It didn't matter why she loved him. She just did. 'No,' she whispered.

'Because there's nothing about you I'd want to change. I knew that from the moment we met. You're perfect,' he breathed happily.

And a long time later when he was cradling her head over his heart, he said, 'What do you want to call the baby?'

Sarah knew that that didn't matter either. 'It's your turn to pick the names,' she said on a sigh of contentment, and snuggled closer.

She smiled as Ben tried out one name after another, examining them for advantages and disadvantages. He was still musing over several possibilities when Sarah drifted into sleep to dream the most perfect, wonderful dreams.

Next Month's Romances

Each month you can choose from a world of variety in romance with Mills & Boon. Below are the new titles to look out for next month, why not ask either Mills & Boon Reader Service or your Newsagent to reserve you a copy of the titles you want to buy — just tick the titles you would like to order and either post to Reader Service or take it to any Newsagent and ask them to order your books.

Please save me the following titles:

		Please tick ✓
A HONEYED SEDUCTION	Diana Hamilton	
PASSIONATE POSSESSION	Penny Jordan	
MOTHER OF THE BRIDE	Carole Mortimer	
DARK ILLUSION	Patricia Wilson	
FATE OF HAPPINESS	Emma Richmond	
THE ALPHA MAN	Kay Thorpe	
HUNGARIAN RHAPSODY (This book is free with THE ALPHA MAN)	Jessica Steele	
NOTHING LESS THAN LOVE	Vanessa Grant	
LOVE'S VENDETTA	Stephanie Howard	
CALL UP THE WIND	Anne McAllister	
TOUCH OF FIRE	Joanna Neil	
TOMORROW'S HARVEST	Alison York	
THE STOLEN HEART	Amanda Browning	
NO MISTAKING LOVE	Jessica Hart	
THE BEGINNING OF THE AFFAIR	Marjorie Lewty	
CAUSE FOR LOVE	Kerry Allyne	
RAPTURE IN THE SANDS	Sandra Marton	

If you would like to order these books from Mills & Boon Reader Service please send £1.70 per title to: Mills & Boon Reader Service, P.O. Box 236, Croydon, Surrey, CR9 3RU and quote your Subscriber No:...(If applicable) and complete the name and address details below. Alternatively, these books are available from many local Newsagents including W.H.Smith, J.Menzies, Martins and other paperback stockists from 11th September 1992.

Name:..

Address:...

....Post Code:.........................

To Retailer: If you would like to stock M&B books please contact your regular book/magazine wholesaler for details.

You may be mailed with offers from other reputable companies as a result of this application. If you would rather not take advantage of these opportunities please tick box ☐

Mills Boon

Forthcoming Titles

DUET
Available in August

The Emma Darcy Duet

**STRIKE AT THE HEART
THE POSITIVE APPROACH**

The Anne Mather Duet

**BURNING INHERITANCE
TRIAL OF INNOCENCE**

BEST SELLER ROMANCE
Available in September

HIDDEN TREASURES Emma Goldrick

THE KISSING GAME Sally Wentworth

MEDICAL ROMANCE
Available in September

GYPSY SUMMER Laura MacDonald

THE BECKHILL TRADITION Lilian Darcy

THE DOCTORS AT SEFTONBRIDGE Janet Ferguson

A MIDWIFE'S CHOICE Margaret Holt

Available from Boots, Martins, John Menzies, W.H. Smith,
most supermarkets and other paperback stockists.

Also available from Mills & Boon Reader Service,
P.O. Box 236, Thornton Road, Croydon, Surrey CR9 3RU.

Readers in South Africa - write to:
Book Services International Ltd, P.O. Box 41654,
Craighall, Transvaal 2024.